Biology
The Web of Life

■ ■

UNIT 2 REVIEW MODULE

Scott Foresman
AddisonWesley

Editorial Offices: Menlo Park, California • Glenview, Illinois
Sales Offices: Reading, Massachusetts • Atlanta, Georgia • Glenview, Illinois •
Carrollton, Texas • Menlo Park, California

http://www.sf.aw.com
http://www.biosurf.com

To the Teacher

Each Unit Review Module contains Section Reviews, Activity Recordsheets, Interpreting Graphics Exercises, Critical Thinking Exercises, Enrichment Topics, Vocabulary Reviews, Tests, and Lab Practical Exams. The components of the Unit Review Module can be photocopied and distributed to students.

- The Section Reviews offer students the opportunity to review the content and concepts in each numbered section of the Student Edition.

- Activity Recordsheets provide students with space to record data and answer questions presented in the *Lab Zone Do It* and *Investigate It* activities in the Student Edition.

- The Interpreting Graphics exercises challenge students to analyze processes, data, or information presented graphically.

- The Critical Thinking Exercises apply one or more critical thinking skills, many of which are described in the Reference Bank of the Student Edition. Students of all levels, backgrounds and abilities can benefit from practicing the thinking skills presented in these worksheets.

- The Enrichment Topics are essays that expand on topics from the Student Edition, by applying underlying concepts to real-world problems. Each topic has an open-ended evaluation section that promotes critical thinking, writing skills, and creative problem solving.

- The Vocabulary Reviews give students the opportunity to review key vocabulary terms while completing a variety of different exercises.

- There are two tests for each chapter. Test A has 25 multiple choice questions that test students' understanding of key terms, content, and concepts. Test B offers questions that challenge students to explain, describe, compare, interpret, and apply higher order thinking skills.

- The Lab Practical Exams enable teachers to assess the laboratory skills of students, to provide an alternative means to assess the progress of students, and to give students the opportunity to demonstrate what they have learned during their laboratory sessions.

Cover Photograph: Tim Davis / Davis-Lynn Images

in the United States of America. Published simultaneously in Canada.

1-32117-3

6 7 8 9 10 ML 01 00 99 98 97

Unit 2 Review Module

Contents
....

Section	Student Activities/Features	Teacher's Resource Package
6.1 Patterns of Inheritance **Objectives** ■ Distinguish between dominant traits and recessive traits ■ Analyze the results of Mendel's experiments with three generations of garden peas	**Lab Zone Discover It!** *Find Characteristics That Are Inherited*, p. 129 **Everyday Biology** *Bloodlines*, p. 130	**Unit 2 Review Module** ■ Section Review 6.1 ■ Enrichment Topics 6-1 and 6-2
6.2 Principles of Inheritance **Objectives** ■ Explain the chromosome theory of heredity ■ Summarize Mendel's laws	**Lab Zone Think About It!** *Predicting Parakeet Color*, p. 135 **Lab Zone Do It!** *Can You Illustrate the Law of Dominance?* p. 137	**Unit 2 Review Module** ■ Section Review 6.2 ■ Activity Recordsheet 6-1
6.3 Genetics and Predictions **Objectives** ■ Explain how probability is used in genetic predictions ■ Construct a Punnett square for monohybrid and dihybrid crosses ■ Infer genotype by using a test cross	**Lab Zone Do It!** *How Is Genetics Related to Probability?* p. 139	**Unit 2 Review Module** ■ Section Review 6.3 ■ Activity Recordsheet 6-2 ■ Interpreting Graphics 6 **Consumer Applications** 6-1 and 6-2 **Laboratory Manual,** Lab 13: "Genetics and Chance"
6.4 Predictions and People **Objectives** ■ Interpret pedigrees and understand their purpose ■ Contrast dominant and recessive genetic disorders ■ Identify some methods used to determine the likelihood of a genetic disorder occurring in offspring	**STS: Frontiers in Biology** *Genetic Counseling*, p. 144 **Everyday Biology** *Ears to You!* p. 145 **Lab Zone Investigate It!** *Using a Pedigree*, p. 146	**Unit 2 Review Module** ■ Section Review 6.4 ■ Activity Recordsheet 6-3 ■ Critical Thinking Exercise 6 ■ Enrichment Topic 6-3 **Laboratory Manual,** Lab 14: "Pedigree Analysis" **Biotechnology Manual,** Lab 10: "Assessing Genetic Variation in Humans" **Issues and Decision Making** 6-1
6.5 Difficult Predictions **Objectives** ■ Compare and contrast patterns of inheritance that do not follow Mendel's laws ■ Explain how traits are influenced by the environment	**Everyday Biology** *Hold the Eggs*, p. 148 **In the Community** *Blood Drive*, p. 148 **STS: Issues in Biology** *The Genetics of Behavior*, p. 152	**Unit 2 Review Module** ■ Section Review 6.5 ■ Enrichment Topic 6-4 ■ Vocabulary Review 6 ■ Chapter 6 Tests **Issues and Decision Making** 6-2

Technology Resources

Internet Connections

Within this chapter, you will see the bioSURF logo. If you and your students have access to the Internet, the following URL address will provide various Internet connections that are related to topics and features presented in this chapter:

http://genetics.biosurf.com

You can also find relevant chapter material at **The Biology Place** address:

http://www.biology.com

CD-ROMs

Biología: la telaraña de la vida, (Spanish Student Edition) Chapter 6
Teacher Resource Planner, Chapter 6 Supplements
Interactive Biological Simulations
- Punnett Squares
TestWorks CD-ROM
- Chapter 6 Tests

Videodiscs

Animated Biological Concepts Videodiscs
- Segregation of Chromosomes

Overhead Transparencies

- Punnett Square, #14
- Dihybrid Cross, #15

Videotapes

Biology Alive! Video Series
Rewind: The Web of Life Reteach Videos

Planning for Activities

STUDENT EDITION

Lab Zone
Discover It! p. 129
- pencil
- paper
- graph paper

Lab Zone Do It!
p. 137
- buttons: two different colors
- paper
- pencil

Lab Zone Do It!
p. 139
- coins
- pencil
- paper

TEACHER'S EDITION

Class Activity, p. 131
Diagramming the parts of a flower
- variety of flowers

Teacher Demo, p. 134
Modeling chromosome pairs
- black and red plastic disks

Class Activity, p. 135
Dominant and recessive alleles
- permanent marker
- paper

Teacher Demo, p. 147
Testing for dominance
- bottle
- red beads
- white beads

Teacher Demo, p. 148
Expressing incomplete dominance
- plastic plates
- variously-colored beans

Patterns of Inheritance
Section Review

6.1
....

The Big Idea!
Traits are inherited in a consistent pattern. 6.1–6.2

Concepts
- Genetics is the study of heritable characteristics or traits.
- Gregor Mendel used mathematics to study the inheritance of traits.
- Alleles are alternate forms of a gene. In a hybrid organism, the dominant allele is expressed.

Words
genetics   trait   purebred   hybrid   dominant trait   recessive trait   genes
alleles

PART A

1. What is the study of genetics?

_____

2. What is a trait?

_____

3. Why did Gregor Mendel choose to study the pea plant for his genetic experiments?

_____

_____

4. What is the difference between a purebred and a hybrid?

_____

_____

_____

5. Explain the difference, according to Mendel, between a dominant and recessive trait in an F_1 hybrid.

_____

_____

_____

6. Explain the concept of blending.

_____

_____

_____

7. What did Mendel find in about 25 percent of the pea plant's F_2 generations?

Unit 2 Review Module

PART B

Match each term in Column B with its description in Column A. Write the letter of the correct term on the line provided.

COLUMN A

COLUMN B

_____ **1.** A(n) ____ is a characteristic that can be passed from parent to offspring.

a. purebred

b. first filial

_____ **2.** Mendel called his first generation of offspring the ____ generation.

c. genes

_____ **3.** ____ are sections of chromosomes that code for a trait.

d. alleles

e. blending hypothesis

_____ **4.** A(n) ____ receives different genetic traits from each parent.

f. genotype

_____ **5.** Prior to Mendel's work, scientists explained inheritance by the ____.

g. parental

_____ **6.** One of the tools that Gregor Mendel used to explain his hypothesis was ____.

h. second filial trait

i. dominant trait

j. hybrid

_____ **7.** A trait that appears or is expressed in the F_1 generation is a(n) ____.

k. recessive trait

_____ **8.** The genetic makeup of an organism is called its ____.

l. mathematics

m. trait

n. phenotype

August Weismann
Enrichment Topic

In 1886, before the writings of Gregor Mendel had been noticed by the scientific community, researcher August Weismann wrote a book on germ plasm. Weismann's germ plasm theory introduced the idea that all living things contain a special hereditary substance.

Weismann was born in 1834 in Germany. He received medical training but turned to zoological research. Weismann developed his germ plasm theory while he was studying the sex cells of the hydrozoa. He believed that the germ cells of animals contained something that was essential for the species to continue. He thought that this substance must be passed on through generations.

Weismann theorized that since two parents contribute two different hereditary substances, the fertilized egg would have a combination of hereditary material. He noted that the hereditary material would continually increase over generations, doubling each time, unless there was some stage where the material was reduced. He predicted a division of the material at some phase of germ plasm development.

Weismann's germ plasm theory is still valid today, although the terminology has changed. Today, we call germ plasm genes. Weismann's mysterious substance is made up of chromosomes and DNA. And, as Weismann predicted, the division of genetic material does occur during meiosis.

In addition to observing hydrozoa, Weismann conducted experiments investigating the inheritance of acquired characteristics. He supported many of Darwin's ideas, and opposed the idea that offspring can inherit characteristics acquired during their parents' lifetimes. Weismann experimented by cutting off the tails of five generations of mice. Since all the mice born to the tailless parents had tails, Weismann was able to support his hypothesis that acquired characteristics were not inherited.

EVALUATION   *Review Mendel's work on genetics in Chapter 6 of your textbook. One the lines provided, write a brief essay comparing and contrasting the work of Mendel and Weismann. Be sure to include answers to the following in your essay:*

- Whose work was carried out first? Whose work was recognized first?
- What experiments did each scientist use to investigate his theories?

_____

_____

_____

_____

_____

_____

_____

_____

_____

_____

_____

_____

_____

Corn Breeding: The Double Cross
Enrichment Topic

The development of hybrid corn is a testament to both practical experience and scientific knowledge. Corn originated in America, where it was first developed by Native Americans in the Mexican highlands. Corn formed the agricultural basis of the Aztec civilization.

The first European settlers of North America—the Spanish, French, and English—all quickly adopted the crop. The English settlers first received corn, a hard-kerneled, early-maturing variety called flint corn, from northern Native Americans. The Native Americans in the south central areas grew a soft-kerneled, high-yielding, late-maturing variety, called dent corn. These were just two of the many varieties of corn developed by Native Americans.

In 1812, a farmer named John Lorain experimented by crossbreeding the dent and flint varieties of corn. He found that certain crosses resulted in a corn with a better yield than the flint variety, and also with many of the desirable characteristics of the dent variety. Other farmers followed the example set by Lorain. For many years, the most popular corn in the midwestern U.S. was a cross between flint and dent varieties.

In the 1800s, both Gregor Mendel and Charles Darwin experimented with breeding corn. While Darwin is most well known for his theory of evolution, he also discovered that inbreeding in plants usually reduces a plant's vigor. Crossbreeding, he found, increases its vigor.

In 1908, George Harrison Shull found that plant self-fertilization produced weakened plants. When he crossbred inbred strains, however, the plants' vigor was restored. At about the same time, other scientists found that although inbreeding could increase the protein content in corn, the overall yield declined.

In 1917, Donald F. Jones of the Connecticut Agricultural Experiment discovered a practical balance to inbreeding and crossbreeding. Jones' solution is called the "double cross." The double cross was the basic technique used to develop modern hybrid corn. Jones' method uses four inbred corn lines. Instead of simply crossing two lines, he crossed lines A and B, and C and D. Then he crossed AB and CD. The resulting corn is called a double-cross hybrid. The hybrid seed changed much of American agriculture. Inbred lines can be chosen for desirable traits, and undesirable traits can be diminished or eliminated by crossbreeding. The first commercial hybrid corn was produced in 1921.

EVALUATION   *In the space provided, draw a diagram illustrating the double-cross method of corn breeding. Draw the corn plants A, B, C, and D, and illustrate how they were bred by Jones.*

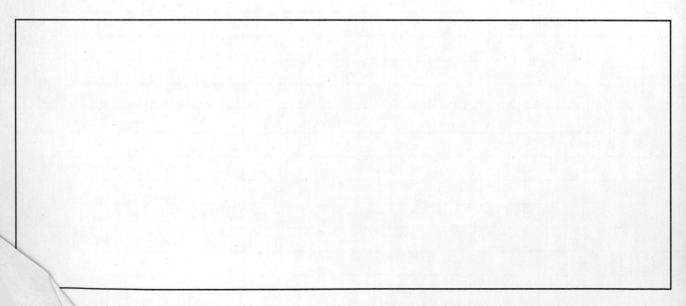

Principles of Inheritance

Section Review

6.2

The Big Idea!

Traits are inherited in a consistent pattern. 6.1–6.2

Concepts

- The chromosome theory of heredity states that the inheritance of traits is controlled by genes, which are located on chromosomes.
- The genotype of an organism is all the alleles for a trait; the phenotype is the trait.
- The Law of Segregation describes how chromosomes separate during meiosis.
- The Law of Independent Assortment states that gene pairs separate independently of each other.
- The Law of Dominance States that the dominant allele, if present, will be expressed.

Words

chromosome theory of heredity   genotype   phenotype   homozygous   heterozygous

PART A   *Complete the table.*

Genotype and Phenotype of Mendel's Pea Plants

Genotype	Heterozygous or Homozygous	Phenotype
GG	1.	2.
3.	4.	yellow pods
5.	heterozygous	6.

PART B

1. Explain the significance of uppercase and lowercase letters when used to represent genotypes.

_____

_____

2. Define genotype and phenotype.

_____

_____

3. Give an example of pea plants that have the same phenotype but different genotypes.

_____

_____

4. Explain the Law of Segregation.

_____

_____

5. Explain the Law of Dominance.

_____

_____

_____

6. Explain the Law of Independent Assortment.

_____

_____

_____

PART C *Read the following scenarios and decide which of Mendel's laws of inheritance is illustrated. Write the name of the law on the lines provided.*

1. A farmer wants to grow only short corn plants. Short stature in corn is caused by a recessive allele. The farmer notices that most of his corn plants are tall.

_____

2. The farmer crosses two tall plants. The cross results in three tall plants and one short plant. The farmer hypothesizes that the factor for short plants was present in the tall plants, and that this factor passed separately from the factor for tall plants.

_____

3. The farmer crosses tall corn plants that have yellow kernels with short corn plants that have green kernels. Some of the resulting offspring are short but have yellow kernels.

_____

Do It! Can You Illustrate the Law of Dominance?

Activity Recordsheet

6-1

• •

Each offspring gets one gene from each parent. You can model the offspring if you . . .

Try This

1. Use four buttons, two of one color and two of another color, to represent two alleles. Select a color and the dominant trait; the other color is the recessive trait. Make a model to represent two parents, each of whom is heterozygous for the trait.

2. Each parent will give the offspring one allele for this trait. What are the possible combinations? Move the buttons to model each combination. Be sure to return the buttons to their original parent model. Record each of your offspring models.

3. Repeat until you have made all possible models.

Analyze Your Data

1. How many different arrangements of alleles can occur in the offspring of these parents?

_____

2. How many ways can an offspring receive the same alleles (one of each color) as the parent?

_____

3. How are Mendel's three laws represented in this activity?

_____

_____

_____

Genetics and Predictions
Section Review

6.3

- -

The Big Idea!
There are patterns of inheritance that make some traits predictable. 6.3–6.5

Concepts
- Scientists use probability to predict traits in offspring.
- A Punnett square organizes information in order to make genetic predictions.

Words
Punnett square   test cross

PART A

1. What is probability?

_____

_____

2. Explain what probability each of the following represents.

  a. $P = \frac{2}{3}$

  b. $P = \frac{4}{5}$

3. Why is probability useful in biology?

_____

_____

PART B   *Calculate the probability of the following situations. Show your calculations. You may use a Punnett square if you wish.*

1. A pea plant with the genotype *GG* is crossed with a pea plant with the genotype *Gg*. What is the probability that an F_1 plant will have the genotype *Gg*? Explain.

2. Two pea plants with the genotype *Gg* are crossed. What is the probability that an F_1 plant will have the genotype *gg*? Explain.

3. Two pea plants with the genotype *Gg* are crossed. What is the probability that an F_1 plant will have the genotype *Gg*? Explain.

PART C   *Complete the following Punnett squares. The Punnett square in Figure 1 should show a monohybrid cross of heterozygous pea plants with axial flower positions. Figure 2 should show a dihybrid cross of heterozygous pea plants with axial flower positions and gray seedcoat colors.*

F: allele for axial flower position

f: allele for terminal flower position

S: allele for gray seed coat color

s: allele for white seed coat color

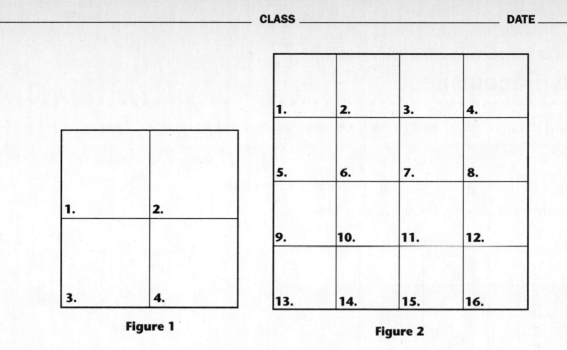

Figure 1

Figure 2

PART D *Use your responses for Part C to complete the following.*

1. Explain how a monohybrid cross and a dihybrid cross differ. _____

_____

2. What is a test cross? _____

_____

_____

3. How many plants in Figure 1 would have an axial flower position? _____

4. How many plants in Figure 1 would have a terminal flower position? _____

5. What is the phenotypic ratio for Figure 1? _____

6. What is the genotypic ratio for Figure 1? _____

7. What genotypes represent axial flowers with gray seedcoats in Figure 2? _____

_____

8. How many plants with terminal flowers and gray seedcoats result from the cross in
Figure 2? _____

9. How many plants with terminal flowers with white seed coats result from the cross
in Figure 2? _____

10. What is the phenotypic ratio for the dihybrid cross? _____

Do It! How Is Genetics Related to Probability?

Activity Recordsheet

6-2

You can use a Punnett square and two coins to learn more about probability if you . . .

Try This

1. Toss a coin 20 times. Record your results, heads *(H)* and tails *(T)*.

2. Draw a Punnett square like the one shown here.

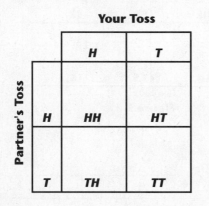

Your Toss

	H	T
H	HH	HT
T	TH	TT

Partner's Toss

3. With a partner, toss two coins at the same time. Repeat 50 times and record each toss *(HH, HT, TH, TT)*. Make sure that you note when you get heads and your partner gets tails *separately* from when you get tails and your partner gets heads. Add up the number of times you get each combination and fill in your Punnett square.

Analyze Your Data

1. How does tossing one coin relate to gamete separation?

_____

_____

2. Based on your 50 tosses of two coins, what is the probability of one coin coming up heads and the other coming up tails?

_____

16 *Unit 2 Review Module*

Interpreting Graphics

6

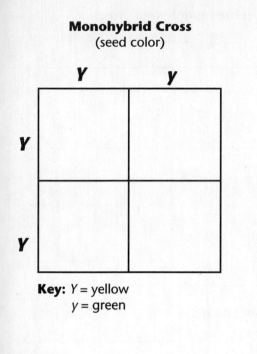

Monohybrid Cross
(seed color)

Key: Y = yellow
y = green

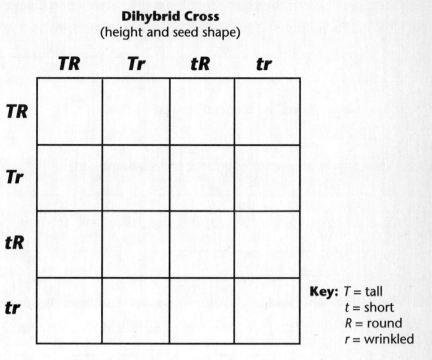

Dihybrid Cross
(height and seed shape)

Key: T = tall
t = short
R = round
r = wrinkled

PART A *Complete the following.*

1. Complete the Punnett square for the monohybrid cross.

2. Complete the Punnett square for the dihybrid cross.

3. Circle the allele of the parent that is heterozygous for seed color in the monohybrid cross.

4. How does a monohybrid cross differ from a dihybrid cross?

_____

_____

5. In pea plants, is yellow or green seed color dominant?

_____

6. In pea plants, are round or wrinkled seeds dominant?

_____

7. Write the genotypes of the offspring that result from the monohybrid cross shown.

_____

_____

8. Write the phenotypes of the offspring that result from the monohybrid cross.

_____

_____

9. How many homozygous yellow offspring will result from the monohybrid cross?

_____

10. How many heterozygous yellow offspring will result from the monohybrid cross?

_____

11. How many of the offspring produced in the dihybrid cross will be homozygous tall?

_____

12. How many of the offspring produced in the dihybrid cross will be heterozygous round?

_____

13. Write the phenotypes that resulted from the dihybrid cross.

_____

_____

14. Explain the different between a phenotype and a genotype.

_____

_____

_____

Predictions and People
Section Review

6.4

∙∙∙

The Big Idea!
There are patterns of inheritance that make some traits predictable. 6.3–6.5

Concepts
- Pedigrees are used to trace the history of traits among relatives.
- Genetic counselors help identify the likelihood of a trait being passed to offspring.

Words
pedigree   carrier

PART A *Match each term in Column B with its description in Column A. Write the letter of the correct term on the line provided.*

COLUMN A

_____ **1.** fatal genetic disorder that results in an inability to break down lipids, causing an accumulation of lipids in the brain

_____ **2.** condition that results from the inability to produce melanin

_____ **3.** genetic disorder that results in an excessive secretion of thick mucus in the respiratory system

_____ **4.** genetic disorder that results in an inability to break down an amino acid found in milk

_____ **5.** fatal genetic disorder that involves deterioration of the nervous system, particularly the brain

COLUMN B

a. albinism

b. Huntington disease

c. cystic fibrosis

d. phenylketonuria

e. Tay-Sachs disease

PART B

1. What type of genetic disorder are Tay-Sachs disease and cystic fibrosis examples of?

_____

2. Give an example of a dominant-allele disorder.

_____

3. How do geneticists develop a human pedigree?

_____

_____

4. How is the information found in the pedigree used?

_____

_____

PART C *This pedigree traces the inheritance of alkaptonuria, a chemical disorder which colors the urine and body tissues. Examine the pedigree chart and answer the questions that follow.*

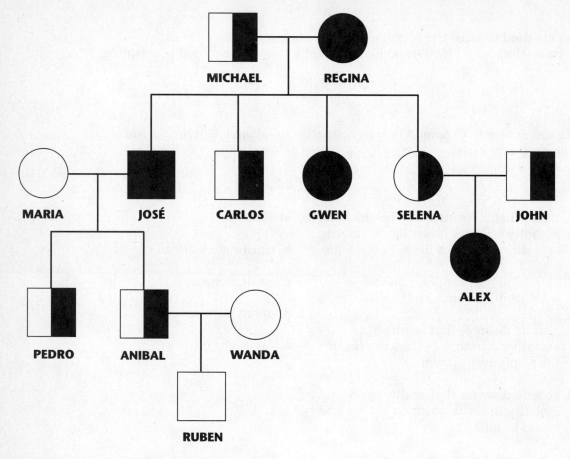

1. Which family members have alkaptonuria?

_____

2. Which family members are carriers for alkaptonuria?

_____

3. Is alkaptonuria a dominant or recessive disorder? Explain.

_____

_____

_____

Investigate It! Using a Pedigree
Activity Recordsheet

6-3

▪▪

Propose a Hypothesis

Form a hypothesis concerning whether the allele for deafness is dominant or recessive.

_____

_____

What You Will Do
Use a pedigree chart to determine parents' genotypes.
Skills You Will Use
Observing, recording data, predicting
What You Will Need
Pencil and paper

Conduct Your Experiment

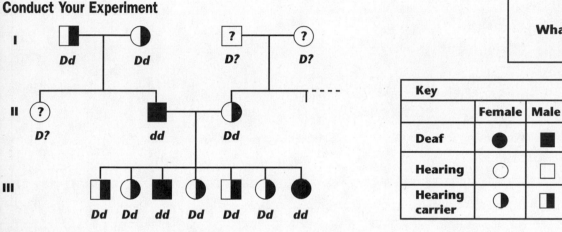

Key		
	Female	**Male**
Deaf	●	■
Hearing	○	□
Hearing carrier	◑	◪

1. Copy the pedigree and the key onto a piece of paper and study it. Label each individual in the pedigree as hearing, hearing carrier, or deaf.

2. Look for a pattern in the inheritance of the trait. Does the trait skip generations or show up in each generation? Does it affect all members of any generation?

3. Use what you know about inheritance to infer the genotype and phenotype of each individual with a question mark. Write the phenotypes and genotypes on your pedigree.

Analyze Your Data

1. What must be the genotype of a family member with deafness? Can a deaf family member have more that one genotype? Why or why not?

_____

_____

2. What are the phenotypes and genotypes of the individuals with question marks? How did you arrive at your conclusions?

_____

_____

3. If carriers were deaf, would this pedigree look different? Explain your answer.

_____

_____

Draw Conclusions

On a separate sheet of paper describe what you have concluded about the dominant or recessive inheritance of deafness in this family. Write a paragraph discussing what you learned in this activity. Support your conclusion with your observations.

Design a Related Experiment

In the space below, prepare a pedigree for three generations of an imaginary family that has another trait.

Pedigree Chart
Critical Thinking   6
. . . .

THE SKILL: Identifying Cause and Effect

A cause-and-effect relationship describes a connection between two variables. The presence of one variable, or cause, triggers the second variable, or effect. When you analyze your observations, it is important to try to identify cause-and-effect relationships that exist among the variables.

Albinism is a hereditary disorder that occurs in human beings and many species of plants and animals. An organism with this disorder cannot make pigment in some or all of its body parts. As a result, the organism has abnormally light coloring. Albinism is caused by a recessive gene. This disorder occurs in an organism that has inherited a recessive allele for the trait from each parent.

The pedigree chart below illustrates the occurrence of albinism in three generations of a family. Use the chart to answer the questions that follow.

Pedigree Chart for Albinism

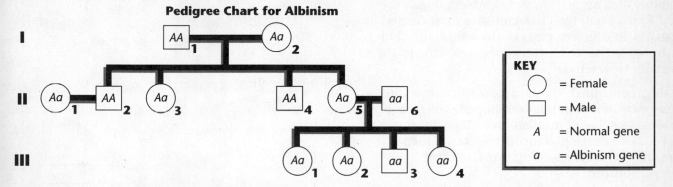

APPLICATION   *Write a complete answer to each question. Use additional pieces of paper if necessary.*

1. Can a person with albinism have more than one genotype? Explain your answer.

_____

2. What are the phenotypes of the second generation of this family?

_____

3. Suppose individual II-3 married a male who was homozygous dominant for this trait. Is it likely that any of their offspring will show the disorder? Explain why.

_____

4. Identify the members of the third generation who show albinism. What caused this phenomenon?

_____

5. What genotype would the spouse of individual III-3 have to be to ensure that none of their offspring would exhibit albinism? Explain your answer.

_____

_____

Animal Pedigrees—A Canine Family Tree
Enrichment Topic

Where did the domesticated dog come from? If you look at the family tree shown here, you can see that the canine group began evolving about 40 million years ago from a tiny tree-climbing animal, *Miacis*.

The dog appears to be the first animal domesticated by humans. Evidence found in a cave in Iraq indicates that dogs were initially domesticated during the Old Stone Age, about 12,000 years ago. Tribes used dogs to help with hunting, for protection at night, and for companionship.

After dogs were domesticated, they were selectively bred for particular characteristics. Just as other domesticated animals have been bred, dogs were bred so they had the characteristics most desired by humans. In different parts of the world, the choice of desirable characteristics varied, resulting in the diversity we see today.

As dogs continued to live as human companions, many new breeds of dogs developed, due to natural factors as well as controlled breeding. Different breeds were developed for specific tasks, such as hunting, herding, guarding, working, and companionship.

The basic principles of dog breeding are those that apply to any animal. Breeding pairs are selected for the desirable genes they will pass on. Some characteristics, such as coat color and length, involve single gene inheritance. However, some characteristics depend on more than one gene. A combination of heterozygous parents can produce a puppy with blue eyes even though both parents are brown-eyed. In German Shepherds, white fur color and dark eyes are recessive. Two black or two tan parent dogs can still produce a white puppy.

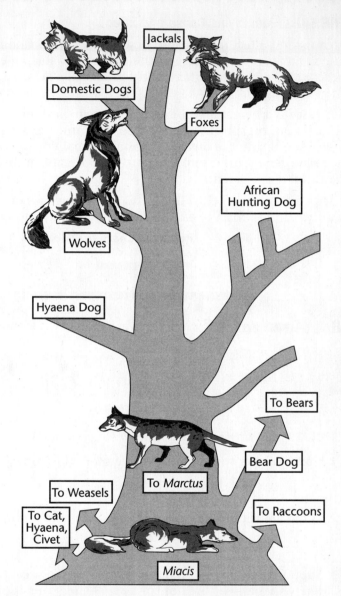

EVALUATION *Research a particular breed of dog and write an essay on how it was bred for its particular characteristics. Be sure to cover the following topics in your essay. Use a separate piece of paper if you need to.*

• Where and when was the dog breed first identified?
• What is its role in the human world? What particular characteristics make the breed especially well suited to this role?

_____

_____

_____

_____

24   *Unit 2 Review Module*

Difficult Predictions
Section Review

6.5

. . . .

The Big Idea!

There are patterns of inheritance that make some traits predictable. 6.3–6.5

Concepts

- Incomplete dominance, codominance, and multiple alleles can result in intermediate phenotypes.
- Genes can have more than two alleles.
- Alleles can have many phenotypic effects.

Words

incomplete dominance   codominance   polygenic trait   multiple alleles   pleiotropy

PART A

1. Explain the concept of intermediate inheritance.

_____

_____

_____

2. How do incomplete dominance and codominance differ?

_____

_____

_____

3. Give an example of incomplete dominance.

_____

_____

4. Give an example of codominance.

_____

_____

5. What is a polygenic trait?

_____

_____

_____

PART B   *Match each type of inheritance listed in Column B with the examples described in Column A.*

COLUMN A

_____ **1.** In Andalusian chickens, a cross between a pure white chicken and a pure black chicken produces offspring that are bluish gray.

_____ **2.** Scientists believe that as many as six sets of genes interact to control skin color in humans.

_____ **3.** In Marfan's syndrome, one gene causes abnormally long legs, fingers, and toes. People with Marfan's syndrome often have heart trouble.

_____ **4.** In sweet clover, there are 200 alleles that prevent flowers from fertilizing themselves.

_____ **5.** Human blood type is determined by the inheritance of two of the three alleles *A, B,* and *O.* When *A* and *B* are both present in the genotype, both alleles are expressed.

COLUMN B

a. polygenic inheritance

b. codominance

c. incomplete dominance

d. pleiotropy

e. multiple alleles

PART C

1. How is the color of a Himalayan rabbit's fur affected by the environment?

_____

_____

_____

2. Describe another example of a way in which environmental conditions affect gene expression.

_____

_____

_____

3. What is meant by "nature or nurture"?

_____

_____

_____

Albinism
Enrichment Topic   6-4

Skin color is the result of three components: melanin and carotene in the skin, and blood in the capillaries of the skin. Some people have no pigment in their skin. This condition is a genetic disorder known as albinism. One out of every several thousand human beings has albinism. Animals are also susceptible to albinism.

Albinism is caused by a melanin deficiency. Melanin is the dark brown pigment that colors skin. Eyes, skin, hair, and other body parts can all be affected by albinism. A completely albino animal has milky-white skin and white feathers or hair. Its eyes often have pink irises. Since no color masks the blood vessels in the eye, light reflected from the iris is red. An albino animal's eyes are usually light sensitive, and often have distorted lenses.

There are several different defects that can cause albinism. One is a complete lack of melanocytes, the cells responsible for pigment. Sometimes, interference in cell migration during embryonic development can cause albinism. Another cause is lack of an enzyme (tyrosinase) that stimulates melanin production. Finally, cell abnormalities can cause albinism.

Albinism is a genetic disorder. The gene for albinism is recessive. Parents can carry the gene without expressing it, so normally pigmented parents may have an albino child. There is currently no method for curing albinism. In humans, proper skin and eye protection and glasses for eye problems can help diminish or prevent problems associated with the characteristics of albinism.

Wild animals that are completely albino are rare because few survive to reproduce. Due to their lack of coloring, albino animals are more visible to predators. Perhaps because they are so rare, some cultures have considered albino animals sacred. A partial albino has white spots on the skin or white patches in the hair. The absence of body pigments in only some areas is called vitiligo.

EVALUATION   *Answer the following questions. Use a separate piece of paper if necessary.*

1. What causes albinism?

_____

_____

_____

_____

_____

2. Choose an indigenous culture, such as Native Americans. Research the culture's attitudes toward albino animals and albino people within the culture. Write a brief essay on your findings.

_____

_____

_____

_____

_____

_____

_____

_____

Unit 2 Review Module   **27**

Vocabulary Review

6

Select the term from the following list that best answers each question.

hybrid   traits

recessive   Punnett square

genes   phenotype

genotype   homozygous

pedigree   chromosome theory of heredity

1. These are traits that are not always expressed in all generations.

_____

2. These are characteristics that are passed from parent to offspring. Examples include height or hair color.

_____

3. This is a blended organism—it has both dominant and recessive traits.

_____

4. This states that chromosomes occur in pairs, and that chromosomes separate independently during meiosis.

_____

5. This is the genetic makeup of an organism. It can be either *TT, tt,* or *Tt.*

_____

6. This is the physical expression of traits.

_____

7. This means that an organism's genotype has two identical alleles.

_____

8. This is a tool that can help you predict types of offspring before fertilization.

_____

9. This helps scientists study how a trait is passed from great-grandparents to their great-grandchild.

_____

10. These are sections of chromosomes that control genes.

_____

Fundamentals of Genetics

Chapter 6

■■

Test A

Choose the best answer for each question and write its letter on the line provided.

_____ **1.** In the 1860s, Gregor Mendel conducted experiments that established the
    a. codominance theory   **c.** bloodline theory
    b. modern genetics   **d.** blending hypothesis

_____ **2.** What does The Law of Independent Assortment state?
    a. Gene pairs always stay together.
    b. Half of an organism's gametes have one allele per pair.
    c. Gene pairs segregate randomly and independently of each other.
    d. One allele is always dominant.

_____ **3.** Probability *cannot* be represented as a
    a. fraction   **b.** ratio   **c.** percentage   **d.** pedigree

_____ **4.** When purebred plants self-fertilize, the traits of the offspring
    a. are the same as the parental traits   **c.** cannot be predicted
    b. are different from the parental traits   **d.** No offspring are produced

_____ **5.** When you flip a coin, what is the probability of getting tails?
    a. $\frac{1}{4}$ **b.** 1   **c.** $\frac{1}{2}$ **d.** 40 percent

_____ **6.** The Law of Segregation states that during meiosis each pair of alleles
    a. is heterozygous   **b.** is tripled   **c.** stays together   **d.** separates

_____ **7.** Type AB blood is an example of
    a. codominance   **c.** incomplete dominance
    b. blending of alleles   **d.** monogenic traits

_____ **8.** What is a trait?
    a. any characteristic that can be passed from plants to animals
    b. any characteristic that can be passed from one species to another
    c. any characteristic that can be passed from parent to offspring
    d. any characteristic that can be passed through a cell membrane

_____ **9.** A gene has multiple alleles if
    a. one individual has many different gene pairs
    b. three or more alleles for the gene are found in a population
    c. incomplete dominance is present
    d. environmental factors affect the expression of a trait

_____ **10.** What did Mendel call a trait that did not appear in an F_1 hybrid?
    a. codominant trait   **c.** recessive trait
    b. parental trait   **d.** dominant trait

_____ **11.** What do Punnett squares show?
    a. actual results of a genetic cross   **c.** the phenotypes of offspring
    b. all possible results of a genetic cross   **d.** only dihybrid crosses

_____ **12.** Eye color, which involves many genetic factors, is an example of
    a. a polygenic trait   **c.** a synthetic trait
    b. a simple hybrid   **d.** single-parent heredity

_____ **13.** Mendel hypothesized that each trait is controlled by a factor, now called a
    a. hybrid   **b.** allele   **c.** recessive   **d.** gene

_____ **14.** Which of the following symbolizes a cross between a purebred green-podded plant with a purebred yellow-podded plant?
    a. *GG* x *gg*   **b.** *gG* x *Gg*   **c.** *GG* x *GG*   **d.** *Gg* x *gg*

_____ **15.** What do geneticists call a genetic cross made to study a single trait?
    a. Punnett square   **c.** gamete study
    b. dihybrid cross   **d.** monohybrid cross

_____ **16.** In incomplete dominance, there are no
    a. homozygous phenotypes   **c.** dominant or recessive alleles
    b. genetic crossings   **d.** intermediate traits

_____ **17.** An allele that expresses itself in a hybrid is a(n)
    a. dominant allele   **b.** allele pair   **c.** pleiotropy   **d.** recessive allele

_____ **18.** A cross that is written *RrGg* x *RrGg* is an example of a
    a. monohybrid cross   **c.** phenotypic cross
    b. dihybrid cross   **d.** test cross

_____ **19.** What is a pedigree?
    a. dominant allele   **b.** phenotype   **c.** inherited trait   **d.** family tree

_____ **20.** Each of the seven traits that Mendel studied occurred in
    a. two distinct, observable forms   **c.** all plants and animals
    b. all plants   **d.** one observable form

_____ **21.** A carrier of Tay-Sachs disease
    a. cannot have children
    b. is homozygous for the Tay-Sachs allele
    c. carries a recessive trait that is not expressed
    d. shows all the symptoms of the disease

_____ **22.** A hybrid is an organism that receives different genetic traits from
    a. different parts of its body   **c.** a single parent
    b. each parent   **d.** changes in the environment

_____ **23.** Because the sickle-cell gene affects more than one trait, it is an example of
    a. pleiotropy   **b.** a genetic cross   **c.** a polygenic trait   **d.** probability

_____ **24.** An organism with two different alleles for a single trait is said to be
    a. homozygous   **b.** heterozygous   **c.** phenotypic   **d.** genotypic

_____ **25.** A pea plant with a purple-flower allele *P* and a white-flower allele *p* is purple because of
    a. the chromosome theory of heredity   **c.** the Law of Dominance
    b. the Law of Segregation   **d.** the Law of Independent Assortment

Fundamentals of Genetics

Chapter 6

• •

Test B

Read each question and respond on the lines provided.

1. You are experimenting with plants that are of the same basic type, but some produce blue flowers and others produce white flowers. You make the following observations about these plants and their offspring:

    I. When crossed only with themselves, the plants with blue flowers produced only blue-flowering plants.

    II. When crossed only with themselves, the plants with white flowers produced only white-flowering plants.

    III. When a purebred blue-flowering plant was crossed with a purebred white-flowering plant, only blue-flowering plants were produced in the F_1 generation.

Given these observations, answer each of the following questions. Explain your reasoning in each case. *(18 points)*

a. Were the original white-flowering and blue-flowering plants purebred or hybrid?

_____

_____

b. Were the blue-flowering plants in the F_1 generation purebred or hybrid, or were there some of each?

_____

_____

c. Is the gene for white flower color dominant or recessive? The gene for blue flower color?

_____

_____

d. If the blue-flowering plants produced in the F_1 generation were crossed with each other, what fraction of the F_2 generation would you expect to be blue flowering? What fraction would you expect to be white flowering?

_____

_____

2. Identify which of Mendel's three laws is illustrated in each of the following. Include statements of the laws themselves. *(15 points)*

a. When a brown duck is crossed with a white duck, all the offspring are brown.

_____

_____

_____

b. When tall, red-fruited berry plants are crossed with short, white-fruited berry plants, every possible combination of height and fruit color shows up in the F_2 generation.

_____

_____

_____

c. An insect that is the offspring of a black-eyed parent and a red-eyed parent produces some gametes that contain the gene for black eye color and some that contain the gene for red eye color.

_____

_____

_____

          Unit 2 Review Module   **31**

3. In the following genotypes, the gene for gray fur is represented as *G* and the gene for white fur is represented as *g*. In each case, state whether the organism is homozygous or heterozygous, and describe the phenotype. (Remember that uppercase letters stand for dominant genes.) *(16 points)*

a. *gg* _____

b. *GG* _____

c. *Gg* _____

d. How many possible phenotypes are there? _____

4. Two bean plants each have the genotype *TtRr*, in which *T* stands for tall, *t* for short, *R* for red flowers, and *r* for yellow flowers. Suppose you cross the two plants. *(24 points)*

a. Is this a monohybrid or dihybrid cross? Explain your answer.

_____

_____

b. Fill in the Punnett square below to show the expected genotypes of the offspring from your cross.

1.	2.	3.	4.
5.	6.	7.	8.
9.	10.	11.	12.
13.	14.	15.	16.

c. How many of each phenotype would you expect among the 16 offspring? Express this as a phenotypic ratio.

_____

_____

5. Explain the difference between polygenic traits and pleiotropy. *(12 points)*

_____

_____

6. Identify each of the following as examples of incomplete dominance, codominance, or multiple alleles. *(15 points)*

a. A bird has inherited alleles for a certain blood type Q and a certain blood type R. The phenotype of the bird shows the full characteristics of both Q and R.

_____

b. The gene for the trait of nail color in a certain kind of bear can be any of three: a gene that produces white nails, a gene that produces brown nails, and a gene that produces black nails.

_____

c. All the offspring of a purebred black dog and a purebred white dog are gray.

_____

Section	Student Activities/Features	Teacher's Resource Package
7.1 Molecule of Heredity **Objectives** ■ Describe the experiments that led to the discovery of DNA as the genetic material in cells ■ Appraise the use of the scientific method in these experiments	**Lab Zone Discover It!** *Make a Model of Genetic Material*, p. 157	**Unit 2 Review Module** ■ Section Review 7.1
7.2 DNA Structure and Replication **Objectives** ■ Describe the structure of DNA ■ Explain the process of DNA replication	**Lab Zone Do It!** *What Is a Twisted Ladder?* p. 163 **Everyday Biology** *DNA Duplicates*, p. 163 **Lab Zone Investigate It!** *Extracting DNA*, p. 164	**Unit 2 Review Module** ■ Section Review 7.2 ■ Activity Recordsheets 7-1 and 7-2 ■ Interpreting Graphics 7 ■ Critical Thinking Exercise 7 ■ Enrichment Topic 7-1 **Biotechnology Manual** ■ Lab 4: "Modeling DNA" ■ Lab 5: "Extracting DNA from Halobacterium Cells" ■ Lab 6: "Extracting DNA from Onions"
7.3 Linked Genes **Objectives** ■ Relate genes, traits, chromosomes, and DNA ■ Contrast gene linkage with Mendelian inheritance ■ Define recombination and mapping	**Lab Zone Think About It!** *Gene Linkage in Imaginary Aliens*, p. 167 **Lab Zone Do It!** *What Does Recombination Look Like?* p. 168	**Unit 2 Review Module** ■ Section Review 7.3 ■ Activity Recordsheet 7-3 **Laboratory Manual**, Lab 15: "Genes in Action: Drosophila Mating" **Biotechnology Manual**, Lab 2: "Modeling the Process of Gene Mapping"
7.4 Sex Linkage **Objectives** ■ Distinguish between autosomes and sex chromosomes ■ Compare and contrast sex-linked, sex-limited, and sex-influenced traits		**Unit 2 Review Module** ■ Section Review 7.4 **Consumer Applications** 7-1
7.5 The Human Gene Map **Objectives** ■ Explain genomes and current genome research ■ Compare monosomy and trisomy and their effects	**STS: Issues in Biology** *The Human Genome Project*, p. 174 **In the Community** *On-Ramp to Biology*, p. 176 **Everyday Biology** *A Cat Called Calico Carl*, p. 176	**Unit 2 Review Module** ■ Section Review 7.5 ■ Vocabulary Review 7 ■ Chapter 7 Tests **Laboratory Manual**, Lab 16: "Clues from the Karyotype" **Issues and Decision Making** 7-1

Technology Resources

Internet Connections

Within this chapter, you will see the bioSURF logo. If you and your students have access to the Internet, the following URL address will provide various Internet connections that are related to topics and features presented in this chapter:

http://genetics.biosurf.com

You can also find relevant chapter material at **The Biology Place** address:

http://www.biology.com

CD-ROMs

Biología: la telaraña de la vida,
  (Spanish Student Edition) Chapter 7
Teacher's Resource Planner, Chapter 7
  Supplements
Interactive Biological Simulations
■ DNA Structure and Replication
TestWorks CD-ROM
■ Chapter 7 Tests

Videodiscs

Animated Biological Concepts Videodiscs
■ Griffith's Experiments
■ DNA Replication
■ Crossing Over
■ Human Sex Determination
■ Nondisjunction

Overhead Transparencies

■ DNA Replication, #16
■ Refining Mendel's Laws, #17

Videotapes

Biology Alive! Video Series
Rewind: The Web of Life Reteach Videos

Planning for Activities

STUDENT EDITION
Lab Zone
Discover It! p. 157
■ one piece of yarn about 6 centimeters (cm) long
■ scissors
■ tweezers

Lab Zone Do It!
p. 163
■ one meter (m) of thick string
■ 20 toothpicks
■ clothing hanger
■ metric ruler

Lab Zone
Investigate It! p. 164
■ fresh beef or pork liver
■ scalpel or dissecting scissors
■ blender
■ 25-mL graduated cylinder
■ saline solution (0.9% NaCl)
■ cheesecloth
■ 250-mL beaker
■ eyedropper
■ liquid soap
■ 95% ethanol
■ glass stirring rod

Lab Zone Do It!
p. 168
■ two colors of modeling clay

TEACHER'S EDITION
Quick Activity, p. 158
Examining sandpapers
■ small pieces of fine-grained, wet-or-dry sandpaper, coarse-grained sandpaper
■ hand lenses

Teacher Demo, p. 160
Identifying objects using shadows
■ overhead projector
■ various objects

Teacher Demo, p. 165
Chromosomes and genes
■ different colors of chalk

Teacher Demo, p. 167
Modeling homologous chromsomes
■ pop-beads or snap-together beads of various colors

Teacher Demo, p. 170
Chromosomes in fruit flies
■ colored chalk

Teacher Demo, p. 175
Different types of chromosomes
■ overhead projector
■ pieces of yarn

Molecule of Heredity

Section Review

7.1

∙∙∙

The Big Idea!

The structure of DNA, the molecule of heredity, enables the molecule to copy itself. 7.1–7.2

Concepts

- Frederick Griffith's experiments showed that genetic material transformed cells.
- Martha Chase and Alfred Hershey proved that DNA is the genetic material of cells.

PART A *Complete Table 1 by writing the results of Frederick Griffith's experiments in the second column.*

Table 1 Griffith's Experiments

Experiment	Result
Live strain S bacteria injected into mouse	**1.**
Live strain R bacteria injected into mouse	**2.**
Dead strain S bacteria injected into mouse	**3.**
Dead strain S bacteria + live strain R bacteria injected into mouse	**4.**

PART B

1. What bacterium was used by Griffith in his experiments?

_____

_____

2. How did the two types of bacteria used by Griffith differ?

_____

_____

_____

3. Describe each of Griffith's four experiments.

_____

_____

_____

_____

_____

_____

4. What did Griffith conclude from his experiment?

_____

_____

_____

5. What important question remained unanswered by Griffith's experiments?

_____

_____

_____

6. Explain the contribution of Oswald Avery to modern genetics.

_____

_____

_____

_____

PART C   *Complete Table 2 by writing the results of Chase and Hershey's experiments in the second column.*

Table 2 Chase and Hershey's Experiments

Experiment	Result
Phage with radioactive protein infects bacteria	1.
Phage with radioactive DNA infects bacteria	2.

PART D

1. a. What type of virus did Chase and Hershey use in their experiments?

_____

b. Why did they chose this type of virus?

_____

_____

2. What did Chase and Hershey discover at the end of their experiments?

_____

_____

_____

3. What conclusion was reached as a result of the work of Chase and Hershey?

_____

_____

_____

DNA Structure and Replication
Section Review
7.2

. . . .

The Big Idea!
The structure of DNA, the molecule of heredity, enables the molecule to copy itself. 7.1–7.2

Concepts
- DNA is composed of nucleotides and is shaped like a double helix.
- A nucleotide has three parts: a sugar, a phosphate, and a nitrogenous base.
- Bases always form complementary base pairs: adenine binds with thymine, and cytosine bonds with guanine.
- Complementary base pairing enables DNA to replicate, or copy itself.

Words

adenine   guanine   cytosine   thymine   double helix   replication

PART A   *Complete the following strand of DNA by placing the letter of the correct nitrogenous base on the line provided. Use **A** for Adenine, **T** for thymine, **C** for cytosine, and **G** for guanine.*

1. _____ – C

2. _____ – C

3. _____ – A

4. _____ – G

5. _____ – T

6. _____ – A

7. _____ – G

8. _____ – T

9. _____ – T

10. _____ – G

11. _____ – A

12. _____ – C

PART B

1. What are Chargaff's rules? _____

_____

_____

2. What contributions to the understanding of DNA were made by Rosalind Franklin? _____

_____

_____

3. What are the three components of a nucleotide? _____

_____

_____

4. How are adenine and guanine different from thymine and cytosine?_____

_____

_____

5. Explain how the double-helix model became the accepted structure of DNA. _____

_____

_____

6. Explain the three main steps in the process of DNA replication.

a. _____

_____

b. _____

_____

c. _____

PART C   *Match the scientist in Column B with his or her contribution to genetics described in Column A.*

COLUMN A

_____ **1.** explored genetic material with mouse experiments

_____ **2.** modeled the DNA molecule as two chains of sugar-phosphate groups running parallel to each and connected by "rungs" of paired nitrogenous bases

_____ **3.** used X-ray crystallography to investigate the chemical structure of DNA

_____ **4.** determined that DNA is most likely the genetic material

_____ **5.** confirmed that DNA is the genetic material

_____ **6.** found that the amount of adenine is always equal to the amount of thymine and the amount of guanine is always equal to the amount of cytosine in a DNA molecule

COLUMN B

a. Oswald Avery

b. Frederick Griffith

c. Chase and Hershey

d. Edwin Chargaff

e. Maurice Wilkins and Rosalind Franklin

f. Watson and Crick

Do It! What Is a Twisted Ladder?
Activity Recordsheet

7-1

- -

DNA is described as a twisted ladder. You can build a model of a double helix if you . . .

Try This

1. Get 1 meter (m) of thick string and 20 toothpicks.

2. Loop the string over a hanger. The string represents the sugar-phosphate backbone of a DNA molecule.

3. Insert the ends of the toothpicks into the two sides of the string. Space them about 4 cm apart. The toothpicks represent the complementary base pairs.

4. Tie the two ends of the string together. Twist the knot a few times, and watch the shape of a double helix form.

Analyze Your Data

1. Why is DNA described as a twisted ladder?

_____

_____

2. How could this twisted-ladder model more accurately represent DNA?

_____

_____

_____

Investigate It! Extracting DNA

Activity Recordsheet

7-2

Propose a Hypothesis

You know that DNA is located in the cell nucleus. Propose a hypothesis about why the materials for this lab can extract the DNA in the liver cells.

_____

_____

_____

_____

Conduct Your Experiment

1. Cut a piece of liver about 2-cm long. Put 10 mL of saline solution and the liver into the blender. Blend until the mixture is uniform. **CAUTION:** Use care when handling scissors and using the blender.

2. Fold two pieces of cheesecloth in half. Use the cheesecloth to strain the liver mixture into a beaker.

3. Use an eyedropper to add approximately 10 mL of liquid soap to the mixture. Mix thoroughly with the glass stirring rod.

4. Measure and record the volume of the soap-liver mixture in the beaker. Multiply this number by 2 and record your result. Add this volume of ethanol to the mixture.

5. Slowly stir the mixture with the glass stirring rod. A white substance will form where the ethanol and liver mixture meet.

6. Watch as the DNA precipitates up through the ethanol. Individual strands of DNA are not visible. Small bubbles will attach to these strands as they move up through the ethanol. Twirl the glass rod slowly in the mixture. Precipitated DNA strands will accumulate and clump together on the rod, forming a visible mass. Record your results.

> **What You Will Do**
> *Extract DNA from liver.*
>
> **Skills You Will Use**
> *Measuring, predicting, collecting and recording data, observing*
>
> **What You Will Need**
> *Fresh beef or pork liver, scalpel or dissecting scissors, blender, 25-milliliter (mL) graduated cylinder, saline solution (0.9% NaCl), cheesecloth, 250-mL beaker, eyedropper, liquid soap, 95% ethanol, glass stirring rod*

Draw Conclusions

1. What does the DNA that you have extracted look like?

_____

_____

2. Now that you have performed this lab, how do you think Miescher first discovered DNA?

_____

_____

_____

Design a Related Experiment

On the lines below, design a lab to extract DNA from another substance, such as onions, dried peas, or yeast.

_____

_____

_____

_____

_____

_____

_____

Interpreting Graphics

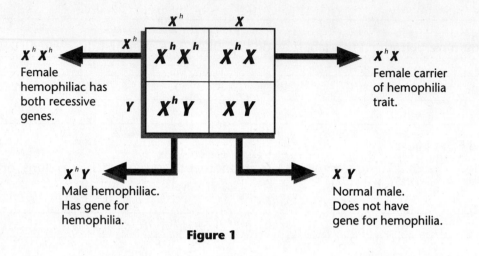

$X^h X^h$
Female hemophiliac has both recessive genes.

$X^h X$
Female carrier of hemophilia trait.

$X^h Y$
Male hemophiliac. Has gene for hemophilia.

$X Y$
Normal male. Does not have gene for hemophilia.

Figure 1

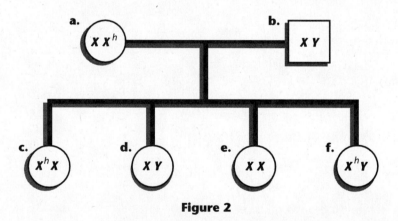

Figure 2

PART A *Answer the following questions on the lines provided.*

1. Explain why one of the female offspring represented in the Punnett square will be a carrier for hemophilia, but the other will have hemophilia.

_____

_____

_____

2. Why is it necessary for a male child to inherit only one gene for hemophilia to develop the disease?

_____

PART B *Complete the following for Figure 2 on the lines provided.*

1. What does the chromosome symbol X^h indicate?

_____

2. Draw a square around each male genotype, and a circle around each female genotype on the diagram.

3. Shade in half of each square or circle that indicates an individual who is a carrier of the hemophilia trait.

4. Shade in all of each square or circle that indicates an individual who has hemophilia.

5. Which males, if any, have hemophilia?

_____

6. Which females, if any, have hemophilia?

_____

7. Which females, if any, are carriers for hemophilia?

_____

8. Is hemophilia a sex-limited or sex-influenced trait? Explain.

_____

DNA Is Not the Only Nucleic Acid

Critical Thinking

THE SKILL: Checking Assumptions

An assumption is a conclusion reached without supporting evidence. Some assumptions
are correct while others are totally invalid. An invalid assumption can prevent you from
completely understanding something. Therefore, it is important to always check assumptions
by looking for supporting evidence.

You probably know that deoxyribonucleic acid, or DNA, is a chemical substance involved
in the passing of traits from parent to offspring. Children inherit DNA from their parents.
Whenever a cell reproduces, its DNA is copied and passed along to the new cell. DNA is like a
blueprint. It does not directly run the processes in an organism. But there is another nucleic
acid involved in cellular reproduction: ribonucleic acid, or RNA. RNA works with DNA to code
for the formation of proteins in the cytoplasm of a cell. Both DNA and RNA are essential to
the passing and expressing of hereditary traits from parent to offspring. The table below lists
chemicals found in DNA and RNA. Use the table to answer the questions that follow.

Components of DNA and RNA	
DNA	**RNA**
Adenine	Adenine
Guanine	Guanine
Cytosine	Cytosine
Thymine	Uracil
Deoxyribose	Ribose
Phosphate	Phosphate

APPLICATION   *Write a complete answer to each question. Use additional pieces of paper if necessary.*

1. What assumption could be made about the nature of DNA and RNA?

_____

_____

2. How does the table help the reader check the accuracy of this assumption?

_____

_____

_____

3. What assumption might be made regarding the transmission of RNA from parent to
offspring?

_____

_____

_____

Rosalind Franklin

Enrichment Topic   7-1

Science and scientific discovery often result from the work of more than one person. In 1962, Watson, Crick, and Wilkins received the Nobel Prize for their research on DNA, four years after the death of a major, but less known, contributor to the project—Rosalind Franklin.

Rosalind Franklin was born in 1920 in London, England. She studied physical chemistry in college and worked with the British Coal Utilization Research Association, where she examined the absorption properties of coal. Her interests led her to a crystallography laboratory in France where she worked with X-ray diffraction. Eventually, Franklin moved back to England to work at King's College, Cambridge, where she applied her knowledge of X-ray techniques to a study of DNA.

When Franklin accepted the position at Cambridge, she believed she was hired to work independently on the DNA project. However, Maurice Wilkins, who recommended her, intended that Franklin would assist him with his own work.

Franklin's X-ray techniques were perfect for the DNA study. She set up a special system with a fine-focus X-ray tube and a high-resolution camera. She used this setup to take high-resolution photographs of single strands of DNA. Franklin took two key photographs. The first clearly showed the two different phases of DNA. The second showed that the DNA backbone was outside the DNA molecule.

While Franklin pursued her work on DNA, Watson and Crick were building DNA models. Without Franklin's permission, Wilkins showed Watson and Crick the photographs Franklin had taken. The photographs provided them with important information about the structure of DNA.

When Watson and Crick completed their DNA models, Franklin rejoiced. Her photographs had confirmed their results. Unfortunately, she was never informed that her work had been essential to the formation of the Watson and Crick DNA models.

Franklin had great difficulty working as a subordinate to Wilkins, and she eventually left the DNA research project. She turned her attention to the study of the structure of plant viruses. Then, at the early age of 37, she died of cancer.

EVALUATION   *Review the information you have been given about the life and work of Rosalind Franklin. Then write an essay (you may use additional resources) that supports or criticizes Wilkins' secret use of Franklin's photographs. Be sure to cover the following points in your essay:*

- Do you think Wilkins deserved to share the Nobel Prize with Watson and Crick? Note that Franklin was already dead, and the prize is not awarded posthumously. In addition, the prize can only be shared three ways.
- Do you think it was ethical of Wilkins to show Franklin's photographs? What if he believed it was actually *his* work, since he believed she was working for him?

Linked Genes
Section Review

7.3

. . . .

The Big Idea!
Genes, sections of DNA that code for a specific trait, are linked together on chromosomes. 7.3–7.5

Concepts
- Linked genes are located in the same chromosome and do not sort independently.
- Chromosomes sometimes cross over during meiosis, resulting in recombination of alleles.

Words

linked genes   crossing over

PART A

1. Describe the experiments with sweet pea plants performed by Bateson and Punnett.

_____

_____

_____

2. What was the unexpected result of these experiments?

_____

_____

_____

3. What did Bateson and Punnett conclude from their experiment with sweet pea plants?

_____

_____

_____

4. What did Thomas Hunt Morgan discover in his experiments with fruit flies?

_____

_____

_____

5. Did the experiments of Bateson, Punnett, and Morgan prove that Gregor Mendel's theory of inheritance was incorrect? Explain your answer.

_____

_____

_____

6. What are linked genes?

_____

_____

7. Explain the effects of linked genes on heredity.

_____

_____

_____

8. Are linked genes always inherited together? Explain your answer.

_____

_____

_____

PART B   *Complete the diagram and answer the questions that follow on a separate piece of paper.*

Figure 1 Crossing Over

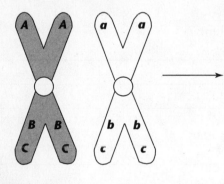   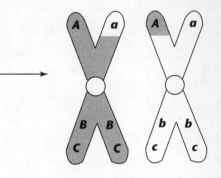

Hair Texture	Eye Color	Hair Color
A = wavy hair	B = brown eyes	C = brown hair
a = straight hair	b = blue eyes	c = blonde hair

1. Draw the crossing over of the two alleles for hair texture that would result in the chromosomes shown in the diagram.

2. Which genes are closer on the chromosomes: hair texture and eye color, or hair color and eye color?

3. Which traits are most likely to be inherited together?

4. Why are the genes for hair texture and eye color more likely to be separated by crossing over than are the genes for hair color and eye color?

5. Why is crossing over important?

6. What are recombinant offspring?

7. Describe how genetic recombination is used to produce genetic maps.

Unit 2 Review Module

Do It! What Does Recombination Look Like?

Activity Recordsheet

7-3

- -

You can model recombination if you . . .

Try This

1. Obtain two different colors of modeling clay.

2. Make one chromosome out of each color of clay. The chromosome should look like duplicated chromosomes at the beginning of meiosis.

3. Using your two clay chromosomes, model the steps of meiosis as shown in Figure 5.11, pages 114–115 of your textbook.

4. Repeat step 3, including crossing over in prophase l.

Analyze Your Data

1. Why did Bateson and Punnett see recombined traits in sweet pea plants?

   _____

   _____

   _____

2. How could recombination help geneticists locate genes on chromosomes?

   _____

   _____

   _____

   _____

   _____

Sex Linkage
Section Review

7.4

● ●

The Big Idea!

Genes, sections of DNA that code for a specific trait, are linked together on chromosomes. 7.3–7.5

Concepts

- Sex chromosomes determine the sex of offspring. All other chromosomes are autosomes.
- The human sex chromosomes are the X chromosome and the Y chromosome.
- Genes located on sex chromosomes are sex-linked genes.
- Sex-limited and sex-influenced traits are controlled by genes located on autosomes, but these traits are affected by sex hormones.

Words

autosomes   sex chromosomes   sex-linked genes   sex-limited traits   sex-influenced traits

PART A

1. Which chromosomes determine the sex of humans? _____

2. How do sex chromosomes differ from autosomes? _____

_____

_____

3. How is sex determined in species that have sex chromosomes? _____

_____

_____

4. List four reasons that *Drosophila* is used in many genetics experiments. _____

_____

_____

_____

5. Describe Morgan's experiments with the *Drosophila* white-eyed male. _____

_____

_____

_____

6. What did Morgan think was peculiar about the F_2 generation? _____

_____

_____

7. What is a sex-linked trait? _____

_____

_____

PART B *Complete the following.*

1. Write the genotypes for the following phenotypes of red-green colorblindness.

a. normal male _____

d. normal female carrying no colorblind alleles _____

b. colorblind male _____

e. normal female carrying the colorblind allele _____

c. colorblind female _____

2. A woman with normal color vision (carrying no colorblind alleles) and a colorblind man have children. Fill in the Punnett square to determine the genotypes of their children.

3. a. In the example above, what proportion of the male children are colorblind?

_____

b. What proportion of the female children are colorblind?

_____

4. Another couple consists of two people with normal vision. In this case, the female carries the colorblind allele. Fill in the Punnett square to determine the genotypes of their children.

5. a. In the example above, what proportion of the male children are colorblind?

_____

b. What proportion of the female children are colorblind?

_____

6. Why must males inherit colorblindness from their mothers?

_____

_____

7. Why is colorblindness more common in males than in females?

_____

_____

PART C *Complete the following on a separate piece of paper.*

1. Explain how sex-linked traits differ from sex-limited traits.

2. Give two examples of traits that are sex-limited.

3. What is a sex-influenced trait?

4. Give an example of a sex-influenced trait.

The Human Gene Map
Section Review

7.5

- -

The Big Idea!

Genes, sections of DNA that code for a specific trait, are linked together on chromosomes.
7.3–7.5

Concepts

- A karyotype is an image showing all of an organism's chromosomes.
- A genome is the base sequence of all of the DNA in an organism.
- The Human Genome Project is the effort to sequence the entire human genome.
- Nondisjunction occurs when chromosomes fail to separate during cell division.

Words

karyotype   genome   nondisjunction   monosomy   trisomy   polyploidy

PART A   *Match each term in Column B with its description in Column A. Place the letter of the correct term on the line provided.*

COLUMN A

_____ **1.** failure of chromosomes to separate during cell division

_____ **2.** photograph of all an organism's chromosomes

_____ **3.** occurs when a zygote has only one copy of chromosome instead of two

_____ **4.** occurs when a zygote has three copies of a chromosome instead of two

_____ **5.** all the DNA in an organism

_____ **6.** nondisjunction in all chromosomes at the same time

COLUMN B

a. trisomy

b. monosomy

c. nondisjunction

d. karyotype

e. genome

f. polyploidy

PART B

1. Explain the process that leads to the production of a karyotype.

_____

_____

_____

2. What can scientists learn from karyotypes?

_____

_____

_____

3. Give an example of a condition that can be discovered using a karyotype.

_____

_____

PART C

1. What are the advantages of polyploidy in plants?

_____

_____

_____

2. Why is polyploidy a disadvantage to animals?

_____

_____

3. Give three examples of polyploid plants that are important to food production.

_____

_____

4. Give an example of a disorder caused by trisomy.

_____

_____

5. What is the Human Genome Project?

_____

_____

_____

6. Why is mapping the human genome important?

_____

_____

_____

7. Describe one concern felt by those who oppose the Human Genome Project.

_____

_____

_____

Vocabulary Review

7

■ ■

Write the letter of the second pair of words that best matches the first pair of words.

_____ **1.** adenine : guanine as _____

    a. purine : pyrimidine   **c.** cytosine : adenine
    b. thymine : cytosine   **d.** DNA : nucleotide

_____ **2.** adenine : thymine as _____

    a. nucleotide : DNA   **c.** guanine : purine
    b. pyrimidine : cytosine   **d.** double helix : shape

_____ **3.** DNA : nucleotides as _____

    a. autosomes : replication   **c.** trisomy : polyploidy
    b. genome : karyotype   **d.** karyotype : chromosomes

_____ **4.** replication : duplicates as _____

    a. linked genes : polyploidy   **c.** trisomy : nondisjunction
    b. crossing over : recombinants   **d.** adenine : thymine

_____ **5.** autosomes : non-matching as _____

    a. sex chromosomes : homologous   **c.** nondisjunction : polyploidy
    b. double helix : genome   **d.** sex chromosomes : sex-linked genes

_____ **6.** linked genes : Morgan as _____

    a. sex chromosomes : Sutton   **c.** trisomy : Punnett
    b. DNA : Watson and Crick   **d.** Replication : Bateson

_____ **7.** sex-linked genes : color blindness as _____

    a. trisomy : replication   **c.** sex-limited : male beard growth
    b. karyotype : genome   **d.** double helix : linked genes

_____ **8.** sex-influenced : baldness as _____

    a. sex-linked : hemophilia   **c.** nondisjunction : genome
    b. polyploidy : color-blindness   **d.** monosomy : Punnett squares

DNA, Genes, and Chromosomes
Chapter 7
■ ■

Test A

Choose the best answer for each question and write its letter on the line provided.

_____ **1.** The fact that the body color and wing shape of the fruit fly do not sort independently
  a. is evidence of linked genes   **c.** disproves the theory of linked genes
  b. makes Punnett squares useless   **d.** is the only exception to Mendelian genetics

_____ **2.** What is the name for genes found only on the X chromosome?
  a. mutant phenotypes   **c.** male-linked genes
  b. sex-linked genes   **d.** mutations

_____ **3.** Having only one copy of a chromosome instead of two is called
  a. trisomy   **b.** replication   **c.** monosomy   **d.** recombination

_____ **4.** By 1952, geneticists Martha Chase and Alfred Hershey had confirmed that the
  molecule of heredity is
  a. a catalyst   **b.** DNA   **c.** protein   **d.** bacteria

_____ **5.** Which process involves the shuffling of genes into new combinations by crossing over?
  a. genetic recombination   **c.** chromosome shift
  b. gene linking   **d.** gene mapping

_____ **6.** White eye color in the *Drosophila* fruit fly is a
  a. nondisjunction   **c.** sex-linked trait
  b. sex-influenced trait   **d.** mutation

_____ **7.** When Griffith mixed live R bacteria with dead S bacteria, the live bacteria took on the
  traits of the dead bacteria. What did he conclude?
  a. Genetic material was transferred.   **c.** Proteins are recessive.
  b. Fertilization had occurred.   **d.** Genotype and phenotype are unrelated.

_____ **8.** Which term describes the failure of one or more pairs of chromosomes to separate?
  a. massive polyploidy   **c.** nondisjunction
  b. genome disruption   **d.** cloning

_____ **9.** Which of the following methods do scientists use to locate genes on chromosomes?
  a. gene strategy   **b.** gene linking   **c.** gene recombining   **d.** gene mapping

_____ **10.** Sex-limited traits are autosomal traits that are expressed
  a. in either sex   **c.** only in embryos
  b. only in one sex   **d.** only on sex chromosomes

_____ **11.** Chargaff's rule states that in DNA, the amount of adenine equals the amount of
  a. guanine and thymine   **c.** guanine
  b. cytosine   **d.** thymine

_____ **12.** What did Rosalind Franklin and Maurice Wilkins use to help reveal the structure
  of DNA?
  a. bacteriophages   **c.** centrifuge analysis
  b. X-rays   **d.** cytosine analysis

_____ **13.** Recombination occurs more frequently between genes that are
     a. close together on a chromosome   **c.** far apart on a chromosome
     b. genetically incompatible   **d.** genetically compatible

_____ **14.** Which is *not* a characteristic of DNA?
     a. four purines per base pair
     b. a "backbone" of sugar and phosphates
     c. two strands of nucleotides
     d. cytosine

_____ **15.** The structure of DNA is a(n)
     a. triple ellipse   **b.** diamond   **c.** double helix   **d.** octagon

_____ **16.** Chromosomes that are not sex chromosomes are called
     a. Y chromosomes   **b.** gene pairs   **c.** X chromosomes   **d.** autosomes

_____ **17.** Fruit flies are ideal for genetic studies because they
     a. rarely reproduce   **c.** live for a long time
     b. are all one sex   **d.** produce large numbers of offspring

_____ **18.** The term *replication* refers to DNA's ability to
     a. twist into a helix   **c.** appear in X-ray photography
     b. make copies of itself   **d.** attack bacteriophages

_____ **19.** Because X and Y chromosomes are nonhomologous, most of the genes on the X chromosome
     a. do not match the genes on the Y chromosome
     b. are homozygous
     c. match the genes on the Y chromosome
     d. are not expressed

_____ **20.** What is the name of the worldwide project to sequence all the DNA in the human body?
     a. DNA Recombinant Project   **c.** Human Genome Project
     b. DNA Project   **d.** Global Sequencing Project

_____ **21.** Which term describes the results of nondisjunction occuring in all chromosome pairs at once?
     a. monosomy   **c.** multiple replication
     b. duplication   **d.** polyploidy

_____ **22.** A sperm carrying a Y chromosome can produce a(n)
     a. male only   **b.** male or female   **c.** female only   **d.** autosome

_____ **23.** In Down syndrome, the individual has three copies of chromosome 21. This is an example of
     a. base pairing   **b.** trisomy   **c.** monosomy   **d.** polyploidy

_____ **24.** Which is *not* one of the four nitrogenous bases in DNA?
     a. adenine   **b.** guanine   **c.** thymine   **d.** benzene

_____ **25.** In human males, about how many sperm carry an X chromosome?
     a. most   **b.** half   **c.** one quarter   **d.** 10 percent

DNA, Genes, and Chromosomes
Chapter 7

• •

Test B

Read each question or statement and respond on the lines provided.

1. a. What was Griffith's contribution to our understanding of DNA? How did he arrive at his conclusions? *(10 points)*

_____

_____

_____

b. What was the contribution of Chase and Hershey to our understanding of DNA? How did they arrive at their conclusions? *(10 points)*

_____

_____

_____

2. a. What are the components of a nucleotide? *(3 points)*

_____

b. List the four nitrogenous bases. Which form complementary pairs? *(3 points)*

_____

_____

c. How do the sugars and phosphates contribute to the structure of DNA? *(3 points)*

_____

_____

d. Explain how the nitrogenous bases are responsible for the structure of the DNA double helix. What role do the bases play in DNA replication? *(6 points)*

_____

_____

_____

3. Explain how nondisjunction can lead to monosomy or trisomy. What kind of chromosomal study would be most useful in detecting either of these conditions? Why? *(15 points)*

_____

_____

_____

_____

4. State whether each of the following describes a sex-linked trait, a sex-limited trait, or a sex-influenced trait. Explain your answers. *(20 points)*

a. The gene that produces a whitening of the coat in older deer is in both males and females. It can be expressed in both sexes, but differently, and is dominant only in the presence of male hormones. Females develop this trait only when they have two genes for it.

_____

_____

b. In one type of bird, the gene that controls nest-building behavior occurs on an autosomal chromosome and is found in both males and females. It is expressed only in the females and is activated by female hormones.

_____

_____

c. In one type of insect, the gene that produces long antennae is found only on the X chromosome.

_____

_____

5. The allele for fringed petals *(F)* is dominant over the allele for nonfringed petals *(f)* in a certain kind of petunia. The allele for orange stamens *(O)* is dominant over the allele for yellow stamens *(o)*.

a. Suppose you cross a petunia of genotype *FFOO* with one of genotype *ffoo*. What phenotype(s) would you expect in the F_1 generation? *(5 points)*

_____

b. Suppose you then cross plants of the F_1 generation. Assuming that the chromosomes for the traits of fringing and stamen color are on separate chromosomes, what ratio of phenotypes would you expect in the F_2 generation? Why? *(5 points)*

_____

c. Suppose the genes for these traits are on the same chromosome. What phenotype ratio would you expect in the F_2 generation, assuming that no genetic recombination had occurred? Explain your answer. *(5 points)*

_____

_____

_____

6. What is the importance of the Human Genome Project? *(15 points)*

_____

_____

_____

Section	Student Activities/Features	Teacher's Resource Package
8.1 From Genotype to Phenotype **Objectives** ■ Describe the process of transcription of DNA to mRNA ■ Demonstrate the process of translation of mRNA to build proteins	**Lab Zone Discover It!** *Identifying Ways to Prevent Skin Cancer,* p. 181 **Lab Zone Do It!** *What Is Your Codon Count?* p. 186 **Lab Zone Investigate It!** *Modeling Protein Synthesis,* p. 187	**Unit 2 Review Module** ■ Section Review 8.1 ■ Activity Recordsheets 8-1 and 8-2 ■ Enrichment Topic 8-1
8.2 Protein and Phenotype **Objectives** ■ Describe the control of gene expression in prokaryotes ■ Appraise the effects of gene control in eukaryotic cells	**Everyday Biology** *Tidy Proteins,* p. 188	**Unit 2 Review Module** ■ Section Review 8.2 **Laboratory Manual,** Lab 17: "Gene Expression and Environment"
8.3 Changes in Chromosomes **Objectives** ■ Explain how mutations can affect proteins and protein synthesis ■ Distinguish between chromosomal mutations and gene mutations	**Lab Zone Think About It!** *From Milk to Wasp: Modeling Mutations,* p. 195	**Unit 2 Review Module** ■ Section Review 8.3 ■ Interpreting Graphics 8
8.4 Genes and Cancer **Objectives** ■ Summarize the role of oncogenes in the development of cancer ■ Identify environmental causes of mutation	**In the Community** *Where There's Smoke . . .* p. 199 **STS: Frontiers in Biology** *Eat Your Vegetables,* p. 199 **Everyday Biology** *Feeling the Burn?* p. 199	**Unit 2 Review Module** ■ Section Review 8.4 ■ Critical Thinking Exercise 8 ■ Vocabulary Review 8 ■ Chapter 8 Tests **Consumer Applications** 8-1 **Issues and Decision Making** 8-1 **Biotechnology Manual,** Lab 13: "A Simulation of DNA Mutations and Cancer"

Technology Resources

Internet Connections

Within this chapter, you will see the logo. If you and your students have access to the Internet, the following URL address will provide various Internet connections that are related to topics and features presented in this chapter:

http://genetics.biosurf.com

You can also find relevant chapter material at **The Biology Place** address:

http://www.biology.com

CD-ROMs

Biología: la telaraña de la vida, (Spanish Student Edition) Chapter 8
Teacher's Resource Planner, Chapter 8 Supplements
Interactive Biological Simulations
- Transcription
- Translation
TestWorks CD-ROM
- Chapter 8 Tests

Videodiscs

Animated Biological Concepts Videodiscs
- DNA Transcription
- Protein Synthesis
- Duplication and Deletion
- Translocation and Inversion
- Point Mutations

Overhead Transparencies

- Transcription, #18
- Translation, #19
- Prokaryotic Control Mechanisms, #20

Videotapes

Biology Alive! Video Series
Rewind: The Web of Life Reteach Videos

Planning for Activities

STUDENT EDITION
Lab Zone
Discover It! p. 181
- old photograph or painting showing people participating in outdoor activities

Lab Zone Do It!
p. 186
- four sheets of paper of four different colors
- scissors
- table or floor

Lab Zone Investigate It! p. 187
- 36 pushpins (5 different colors)
- metric ruler
- 3 strips of corrugated cardboard (18 cm × 3 cm)
- marker

TEACHER'S EDITION
Quick Activity, p. 182
Deciphering a DNA code
- copies of code sheet

Teacher Demo, p. 184
A eukaryote cell
- transparency or wall chart of an eukaryote cell

Quick Activity, p. 188
Gene—on or off?
- flashlight

Teacher Demo, p. 196
Cancer cells and noncancerous cells
- microprojector
- slides of cancer cells and noncancerous cells

From Genotype to Phenotype
Section Review

8.1

The Big Idea!

Genes are sequences of DNA bases that can be translated into proteins or parts of proteins when they are activated. 8.1–8.2

Concepts

- Protein synthesis occurs in two stages: transcription and translation.
- Transcription is the process by which information is copied from DNA into a strand of messenger RNA (mRNA).
- Translation is the process by which the information from nucleic acids is coded for amino acids.
- mRNA splicing occurs between transcription and translation in eukaryotes.

Words

protein synthesis   RNA   transcription   translation   introns   exons   codon   anticodon

PART A   *Match each term in Column B with its description in Column A. Place the letter of the correct term on the line provided.*

COLUMN A

_____ **1.** process of manufacturing proteins

_____ **2.** carries coded instructions for protein synthesis

_____ **3.** makes up the ribosome with other proteins

_____ **4.** section of three bases in tRNA that code for an amino acid

_____ **5.** sequence of three bases in tRNA that complement an RNA codon

_____ **6.** brings amino acids to the ribosome in the correct order to build new proteins

_____ **7.** transfer of information from DNA to RNA

_____ **8.** sequence of genes that are not part of a code for a protein

_____ **9.** short sequence of DNA that codes for a protein

COLUMN B

a. messenger RNA

b. transcription

c. codon

d. ribosomal RNA

e. transfer RNA

f. intron

g. exon

h. protein synthesis

i. anticodon

PART B *Place the steps of protein synthesis in sequential order. Write the correct letter on the line provided.*

1. _____

2. _____

3. _____

4. _____

5. _____

6. _____

7. _____

8. _____

9. _____

a. The two subunits of the ribosome bind to the start codon of an mRNA molecule.

b. mRNA leaves the nucleus and enters the cytoplasm.

c. Completed protein is released and is ready for use.

d. mRNA attaches to two subunits of the ribosome.

e. Ribosome moves along the mRNA and adds more amino acids to the protein.

f. mRNA is transcribed from DNA in the cell nucleus.

g. tRNA bonds with the correct amino acid.

h. Ribosome encounters the stop codon and falls off the mRNA.

i. tRNA carries the amino acid to the ribosome.

PART C

1. List three ways that RNA and DNA differ.

_____

_____

2. How is mRNA manufactured?

_____

_____

3. What is RNA splicing?

_____

_____

4. How does protein synthesis in prokaryotes differ from protein synthesis in eukaryotes?

_____

_____

5. What is the three letter code and name for the amino acid that is the universal start codon?

_____

6. Identify the codons that give the signal to stop the synthesis of protein.

_____

_____

7. What is elongation?

_____

_____

Do It! What Is Your Codon Count?

Activity Recordsheet

8-1

• •

You can become more familiar with the roles of DNA, mRNA, codons, tRNA, and anticodons if you . . .

Try This

1. Take four sheets of paper of four different colors, and assign a DNA base (adenine, thymine, cytosine, guanine) to each color. Cut the sheets into squares about 3 x 3 cm. Mix all the squares.

2. On a table or the floor, place 30 squares in a left-to-right line. Group the squares by threes to represent DNA codons.

3. In your notebook, list the base sequences for these DNA codons, recording from left to right.

Analyze Your Data

1. What are the base sequences for the complementary mRNA codons? List them in your notebook.

_____

_____

2. What would the base sequences be for tRNA anticodons? List them.

_____

_____

3. The universal mRNA start codon is AUG. The three possible mRNA stop codons are UAA, UAG, and UGA. Are there any start or stop sequences among your codons? If so, record them.

_____

_____

NAME _____ CLASS _____ DATE _____

Investigate It! Modeling Protein Synthesis

Activity Recordsheet

8-2

■ ■

Propose a Hypothesis

Propose a hypothesis about the relationship between bases in nucleic acids and amino acids in a model of protein synthesis.

_____

_____

_____

_____

_____

> **What You Will Do**
> *Make a model to show the two processes of protein synthesis.*
>
> **Skills You Will Use**
> *Modeling, collecting and recording data, analyzing, classifying*
>
> **What You Will Need**
> *36 pushpins (5 different colors), metric ruler, 3 strips of corrugated cardboard (18 cm x 3 cm), marker*

Conduct Your Experiment

1. Group the pushpins by color to represent the five bases in DNA and RNA. Use the ruler and marker to divide each cardboard strip into six equal sections. Label the strips "DNA," "mRNA," and "tRNA." **CAUTION:** Pushpins are sharp.

2. Using the color pushpin you have chosen for each base, create the base sequence CCGAGTTAACCGACGTAA on the DNA cardboard strip. Put one codon in each section. Record your results.

3. Align the mRNA strip and the DNA strip. Use pushpins to model the complementary base sequence on the mRNA strip. Record the sequences.

4. Align the tRNA strip and the mRNA strip. Use pushpins to model the anticodons on the tRNA strip. Record these base sequences.

5. Use the table above to determine the names of the amino acids coded for by the mRNA base sequences. Record this information.

Analyze Your Data

1. Which parts of the activity represented transcription?

_____

_____

2. Which parts represented translation? Explain.

_____

_____

3. How would you change your model to show RNA splicing?

_____

_____

_____

Draw Conclusions

How was your model similar to protein synthesis? How is the sequence of bases in nucleic acids related to the sequence of amino acids in proteins?

_____

_____

_____

_____

_____

Design a Related Experiment

In the space below, design an experiment to show how a small change to a DNA or RNA base sequence can change the amino acids synthesized. Consider at least two different types of changes.

Amniocentesis: Early Cell Investigations
Enrichment Topic 8-1

Medical professionals can use several special screening techniques to detect abnormalities while a fetus is still developing in the womb. One such method is ultrasound, a scanning and imaging technique that provides a picture of the fetus.

A second screening technique, amniocentesis, is usually only performed when doctors believe there may be fetal health risks. During this procedure, a small amount of amniotic fluid is removed from the amniotic sac. The fluid is drawn into a hypodermic needle which has been inserted into the mother's abdominal wall. Amniotic fluid contains cells shed by the embryo.

These cells carry the fetal genetic code and can be cultured and examined for genetic abnormalities. For example, Down syndrome can be diagnosed by examining the cultured cells from the embryo.

An examination of the amniotic fluid itself can also provide important information about the fetus. There are certain proteins that, when detected in very high amounts, indicate neural defects. Spina bifida is one defect that can be diagnosed by examining amniotic fluid.

Amniocentesis is usually performed only after the 16th week of pregnancy. Before this time, there are not enough fetal cells or amniotic fluid to examine. Because the cell culture can also take several weeks, the mother may not know the results of the testing until late in her pregnancy.

There are several new techniques that may replace amniocentesis. Chorionic villus biopsy is a procedure used to culture cells from the chorionic membrane, a membrane that is part of the fetus and surrounds the amniotic sac. Both amniocentesis and chorionic villus biopsy involve taking samples from the womb and present risks to the fetus. A new experimental technique involves separating fetal cells from the mother's blood. The fetal cells are examined just as in amniocentesis, but this technique presents no risks to the fetus because the sample is taken from the mother's blood rather than her womb.

EVALUATION *Review the information you have been given about amniocentesis. Then answer the following questions.*

1. Do all pregnant women undergo amniocentesis? Why or why not?

2. Research more about chorionic villus biopsy. In what circumstances is this testing procedure recommended? What are its advantages and disadvantages compared to amniocentesis?

Protein and Phenotype
Section Review

The Big Idea!

Genes are sequences of DNA bases that can be translated into proteins or parts of proteins when they are activated. 8.1–8.2

Concepts

- The function and structure of a cell is determined by the kinds of proteins it makes.
- The control of gene expression is different in prokaryotic and eukaryotic cells.
- Repressor proteins can block transcription when they bind to promoter regions of DNA.

Words

repressor   promoter

PART A   *Complete the following sentences by writing the correct terms from the Data Bank on the lines provided.*

Data Bank		
selective gene expression	activated	DNA splicing
prokaryotes	cell differentiation	cell specialization
eukaryotes	transcription	deactivated
regulated		

1. When a gene is _____ , it synthesizes its specific protein product.

2. No gene expression occurs when a gene is _____ .

3. In _____ , environmental factors primarily control gene expression.

4. In multicellular _____ , each particular type of cell has a specific

structure and function. This is called _____ .

5. One way eukaryotic cell specialization can be controlled is through

_____ , or the selective activation of different genes.

6. Another mechanism that may control gene expression in eukaryotes is

_____ , in which exons are assembled into a complete molecule

in the nucleus of a cell.

PART B

1. What does the Jacob-Monod hypothesis describe?

_____

_____

_____

2. What is a repressor protein?

_____

_____

_____

3. What is a promoter?

_____

_____

4. Explain how a repressor blocks protein synthesis.

_____

_____

5. What happens when an *E. coli* bacterium is in an environment high in lactose?

_____

_____

_____

_____

6. What happens when the lactose is used up?

_____

_____

_____

7. Explain how high levels of protein product block the synthesis of more protein in some prokaryotes.

_____

_____

_____

_____

Changes in Chromosomes
Section Review

8.3

. . . .

The Big Idea!

Changes in DNA can cause changes in phenotype. 8.3–8.4

Concepts

- A change in an organism's DNA is a mutation. A mutation can be beneficial, but it is usually harmful to or has no effect on the organism.
- Four types of chromosomal mutation are deletion, duplication, translocation, and inversion.
- Two kinds of gene mutation, or change in base sequence, are frameshift mutation and point mutation.

Words

mutation   deletion   duplication   translocation   inversion   frameshift mutation
point mutation

PART A   *Match each term in Column B with its description in Column A. Place the letter of the correct term on the line provided.*

COLUMN A

_____ **1.** changes in genetic material that involve all or part of chromosomes

_____ **2.** occurs when a chromosome breaks and a piece of the chromosome is lost

_____ **3.** occurs when a chromosome receives an extra piece from its partner

_____ **4.** occurs when a chromosome or piece of a chromosome attaches to a chromosome in a different pair

_____ **5.** fragment of a chromosome that attaches itself in reverse order

_____ **6.** mutation that occurs in only one nucleotide

_____ **7.** the deletion or addition of nucleotides that disrupts codons

COLUMN B

a. frameshift mutation

b. deletion

c. inversion

d. point mutation

e. chromosome mutations

f. duplication

g. translocation

PART B

1. Describe the two main categories of mutations.

_____

_____

_____

2. Give an example of a deletion mutation.

_____

_____

_____

3. Why are inversion mutations generally less harmful than deletions or duplications?

_____

_____

_____

PART C *Place a check mark (✔) beside each statement that describes a frameshift mutation.*

_____ **1.** can result from a base-pair substitution in which one pair of bases is replaced in a gene

_____ **2.** results from the addition or deletion of nucleotides that changes a codon

_____ **3.** responsible for the bar eye mutation in fruit flies

_____ **4.** can result in the production of an incorrect protein

_____ **5.** has little impact on an organism's structure and function

_____ **6.** responsible for sickle-cell disease

_____ **7.** changes the code copied by mRNA during transcription

PART D

1. Explain why many point mutations have no effect on protein production.

_____

_____

_____

2. How can a point mutation cause protein synthesis to stop prematurely?

_____

_____

_____

3. What did Barbara McClintock discover while studying corn plants?

_____

_____

_____

_____

Interpreting Graphics

Genetic Disorders

Normal Karyotype

Karotype Indicating Down Syndrome

Klinefelter Syndrome (male)

(female)

Turner Syndrome

Inversion

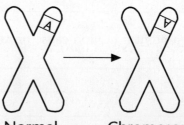

Normal attachment

Chromosome piece turns upside-down

PART A *Complete the following. Use an additional piece of paper, if necessary.*

1. How does the karyotype of a person with Down syndrome differ from a person with a normal karyotype?

_____

_____

2. What is the condition that causes Down syndrome called?

_____

_____

3. What identifies a person as having Klinefelter syndrome?

_____

_____

4. What condition causes Klinefelter syndrome?

_____

_____

5. What condition causes Turner syndrome?

_____

_____

6. Turner syndrome and Klinefelter syndrome both result from the same type of error during meiosis. What is this error called, and which pair of chromosomes is involved?

_____

_____

7. Explain what causes a chromosome inversion.

_____

_____

8. Identify three causes of chromosomal disorders.

_____

_____

_____

_____

Genes and Cancer

Section Review

8.4

The Big Idea!

Changes in DNA can cause changes in phenotype. 8.3–8.4

Concepts

- Oncogenes change a normal cell into a cancerous cell—one that reproduces abnormally.
- Mutagens are environmental factors that cause DNA mutations. Mutagens that cause cancer are carcinogens.

Words

oncogene   mutagen   carcinogen

PART A   *Decide if the following statements are true or false. If the statement is true, write* **True.** *If the statement is false, correct the statement and write it on the line provided.*

1. All cancers result from defective gene control of the production of new cells.

_____

_____

2. An oncogene is a gene that blocks the action of RNA polymerase during protein synthesis.

_____

_____

3. Retinoblastoma, one of the first heritable forms of cancer to be identified, results from the translocation of a gene to chromosome 13.

_____

_____

4. A recessive mutation affects only one chromosome on a homologous pair.

_____

_____

5. People who inherit the recessive mutation for retinoblastoma will not develop the cancer.

_____

_____

PART B   *Complete the following sentences by writing the correct term from the Data Bank on the line provided.*

Data Bank		
chlorofluorocarbons	mutagen	UV radiation
carcinogen	base analogs	tar
repressor proteins	Ames Test	

1. A(n)_____ is a factor in the environment that can affect DNA and cause mutations.

2. A chemical or other agent that causes or tends to cause cancer is known as a(n) _____ .

3. In recent decades, the ozone layer of Earth's atmosphere has been damaged by chemical pollutants called _____ . This damage results in increased levels of _____ , which has been linked to skin cancer.

4. Some carcinogens, called _____ , are incorporated into DNA molecules, thus changing the genetic message.

5. In the _____ , bacteria are exposed to a suspected carcinogen to determine if mutations result.

PART C

1. How is gene therapy used to treat cancer?

_____

_____

_____

2. List three examples of carcinogens.

_____

_____

3. List three ways you can reduce your risk of developing cancer.

_____

_____

_____

DNA and Sun Exposure
Critical Thinking

8

• •

THE SKILL: Analyzing Processes

Analyzing processes can help you understand how a complex system works. When you analyze, you break something down into its parts. You examine how each part contributes to the functioning of the whole. Once you understand how the parts are related, you should be able to explain the process to someone else. Review analyzing processes on page 950 of your textbook.

It is now common knowledge that exposure to the ultraviolet rays (UVR) of the sun can lead to several types of skin cancer and to premature aging of the skin. The intensity of the ultraviolet rays actually alters and breaks certain sections of the DNA strand.

To repair the structural damage done by the sun, a group of proteins, ultraviolet radiation A, B, and C (better known as Uvr A, B, and C) work together with adenosine triphosphate (ATP). In this process, the Uvr ABC proteins attach to the ends of DNA molecules and move along the strand like a zipper. As the proteins advance, they unwind the coiled DNA one section at a time. Once a section of DNA is unwound, it is accessible for repair by another protein, Uvr D. The Uvr D protein cuts out the sun-damaged area, and DNA polymerases create a new section of DNA and insert it into the strand. The energy for this process is derived from the energy-storing molecule ATP.

The more often people are exposed to the ultraviolet rays of the sun, the harder it is for their Uvr proteins to repair their DNA. The results of one study suggest that reduced repair of DNA can lead directly to the development of basal cell carcinoma (BCC), a fatal skin cancer. The ability of DNA to repair itself declines normally with age. This means that, in terms of DNA repair, a teenager who spends a lot of time in the sun is as likely to develop BCC as a person in their 60s!

APPLICATION *Write a complete answer to each question. Use additional pieces of paper if necessary.*

1. How does ultraviolet light damage the DNA of skin cells?

_____

_____

2. What chemical compounds help to repair the damage done to the DNA strands?

_____

_____

3. Describe the process by which these compounds repair the DNA.

_____

_____

_____

_____

_____

4. What two factors contribute to the development of Basal Cell Carcinoma?

_____

_____

Vocabulary Review

8

From each group of terms, choose the term that does not belong and then explain your choice.

1. transcription, translation, RNA, duplication

_____

_____

2. mutagen, promoter, repressor, mRNA

_____

_____

3. tobacco products, chemicals in smoked meats, radiation, refrigerants

_____

_____

4. introns, eukaryotes, prokaryotes, exons

_____

_____

5. codon, proteins, anticodons, tRNA

_____

_____

6. deletion, nucleus, translocation, inversion

_____

_____

7. frameshift mutation, point mutation, duplication, jumping genes

_____

_____

8. oncogene, introns, mutagen, carcinogen

_____

_____

9. transcription, translation, mutation, amino acids

_____

_____

10. inversion, ribosomes, amino acids, tRNA

_____

_____

Protein Synthesis
Chapter 8

■ ■

Test A

Choose the best answer for each question and write its letter on the line provided.

_____ **1.** Duplication is a chromosomal mutation in which part of the chromosome breaks off and is incorporated into its
    a. homologous chromosome   **c.** nonhomologous chromosome
    b. parent chromosome   **d.** base pair

_____ **2.** What is protein synthesis?
    a. process that translates phenotype into genotype
    b. the turning off and on of proteins
    c. process that translates genetic makeup into traits
    d. the transcription of DNA

_____ **3.** What has occurred when a chromosome breaks and a piece is lost?
    a. duplication   **c.** translocation
    b. sex determination   **d.** deletion

_____ **4.** What factors in the environment can cause mutations?
    a. base pairs   **b.** mutagens   **c.** point mutations   **d.** oncogenes

_____ **5.** One difference in gene expression between prokaryotes and eukaryotes is that
    a. expression is more complex in eukaryotes
    b. there are no promoters in prokaryotes
    c. expression is more complex in prokaryotes
    d. no DNA involved in eukaryotes

_____ **6.** It is probable that when DNA is tightly coiled,
    a. prokaryotes can reproduce   **c.** the genes are active
    b. DNA cannot be transcribed   **d.** DNA can be transcribed

_____ **7.** During inversion, a chromosome fragment breaks free and reattaches itself
    a. in all chromosomes at once   **c.** in reverse
    b. in a translocation   **d.** in a nonhomologous pair

_____ **8.** Which is *not* a type of RNA?
    a. messenger RNA   **b.** protein RNA   **c.** transfer RNA   **d.** ribosomal RNA

_____ **9.** A gene mutation can be thought of as
    a. a change in nucleotide sequence   **c.** a perfect copy during replication
    b. an absence of methyl groups   **d.** RNA splicing

_____ **10.** Which of the following is *not* a step in translation?
    a. mRNA attaches to a ribosome.
    b. tRNA transfers amino acids to the ribosome.
    c. Elongation occurs as the amino-acid chain gets longer.
    d. DNA replicates.

_____ **11.** Sickle-cell disease is an example of
    a. point mutation   **c.** frameshift mutation replication
    b. a faulty regulatory protein   **d.** healthy hemoglobin

_____ **12.** What are the noncoding regions of DNA or RNA in eukaryotic cells called?
    a. exons   **b.** codons   **c.** introns   **d.** anticodons

_____ **13.** Which of the following describes a three-base section of mRNA that codes for an amino acid?
    a. codon   **b.** intron   **c.** anticodon   **d.** exon

_____ **14.** What is a gene that causes a cell to become cancerous?
    a. carcinogen   **b.** promoter   **c.** oncogene   **d.** mutagen

_____ **15.** What is the sequence of three bases found on tRNA called?
    a. intron   **b.** anticodon   **c.** exon   **d.** codon

_____ **16.** How does selective gene expression benefit eukaryotes?
    a. amino acid sequencing   **c.** mutations
    b. fertilization   **d.** specialization of cells

_____ **17.** Which of the following is *not* a way to reduce the risk of cancer?
    a. eat a low-fat, high-fiber diet   **c.** avoid all medical tests
    b. use sunscreen   **d.** avoid tobacco products

_____ **18.** American botanist Barbara McClintock won the Nobel prize for discovering that corn genes were moving from one location to another in the chromosome. What is this phenomenon?
    a. transcription   **b.** jumping genes   **c.** genetic linkage   **d.** translocation

_____ **19.** What are the short sequences of DNA that code for a protein?
    a. point mutations   **c.** frameshift mutation
    b. introns   **d.** exons

_____ **20.** What is a repressor?
    a. regulatory gene
    b. anticodon
    c. protein that prevents protein synthesis
    d. inactive gene

_____ **21.** Scientists have determined that the codes for amino acids are
    a. different in humans and bacteria   **c.** different in bacteria and viruses
    b. never the same   **d.** universal

_____ **22.** What is a carcinogen?
    a. mutated gene   **c.** agent that causes cancer
    b. group of cancerous cells   **d.** genetic disorder

_____ **23.** After transcription, mRNA leaves the nucleus and moves to
    a. a universal codon   **c.** a polysaccharide receptor
    b. a ribosome   **d.** a complementary base

_____ **24.** The Ames test helps scientists determine if a substance is a possible
    a. virus   **c.** carcinogen
    b. mutant   **d.** oncogene

_____ **25.** What term describes the deletion or addition of nucleotides that disrupt codons?
    a. frameshift mutation   **c.** nondisjunction
    b. inversion mutation   **d.** point mutation

Protein Synthesis

Chapter 8

▪ ▪

Test B

Read each question or statement and respond on the lines provided.

1. Assume you are working with a scientist who is studying the cell process in which
proteins are synthesized. Part of your job is to summarize the findings.
a. What is the process of making long RNA molecules called? What type of RNA is made
in this process? *(10 points)*

_____

_____

b. How does this process differ between eukaryotes and prokaryotes? *(5 points)*

_____

_____

c. What is the name of the process in which the information in this kind of RNA is used
to build proteins? Specifically, what information is contained in the RNA? *(10 points)*

_____

_____

_____

2. Write the term that is best defined by each of the descriptions below. Use each term once:
oncogene, mutagen, deletion, frameshift mutation, gene mutation, point mutation, and
carcinogen. *(28 points)*

_____ **a.** any change in the way bases are read resulting from a shifting of codons
by one base

_____ **b.** any environmental factor that causes a mutation

_____ **c.** substance that causes cancer

_____ **d.** DNA sequence that causes cancer

_____ **e.** loss of one or more bases from a sequence

_____ **f.** any change in the sequence of nucleotides in a gene sequence

_____ **g.** replacement of only one pair of bases

3. Using the concepts of cell specialization and differentiation, explain the relationship
between the structure and function of a cell and the specific proteins made by that cell.
(4 points)

_____

_____

_____

_____

4. A certain chromosome has the genes P_1, Q_1, and R_1. It is homologous with a chromosome that has the genes P_2, Q_2, and R_2. It is nonhomologous with a chromosome that has the genes S_3, T_3, and U_3. Look at the illustration below. It shows the results of four possible changes, during cell division, of the P_1–Q_1–R_1 chromosome. Identify each change as either normal crossover, deletion, duplication, translocation, or inversion.
(15 points)

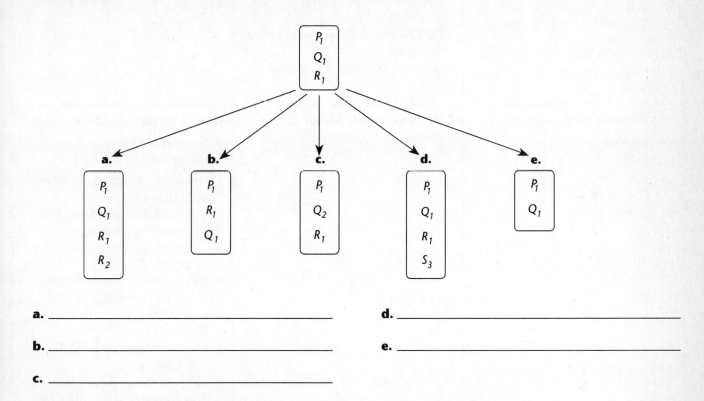

a. _____   **d.** _____

b. _____   **e.** _____

c. _____

5. The table below describes the role of various structures that control gene expression in prokaryotes and eukaryotes. Complete the table by filling in the name of the correct structure for each role described. Possible answers are: repressor, intron, exon, and promoter. *(16 points)*

Role	Structure
a. short gene sequence in eukaryotes that codes for protein	
b. gene sequence in eukaryotes that does not code for protein	
c. region of DNA where RNA polymerase binds in order to initiate transcription	
d. protein that prohibits transcription in prokaryotes and eukaryotes	

6. What are the three ways that a gene can become an oncogene? *(12 points)*

_____

_____

_____

Section	Student Activities/Features	Teacher's Resource Package
9.1 Breeding **Objectives** ■ Compare inbreeding and outbreeding ■ Distinguish between the benefits and dangers of selective breeding	**Lab Zone Discover It!** *Discovering What Makes Fingerprints Unique*, p. 205 **STS: Environmental Awareness** *Seed Banks*, p. 208 **Everyday Biology** *The Ugliest Fruit*, p. 208	**Unit 2 Review Module** ■ Section Review 9.1
9.2 Genetic Engineering **Objectives** ■ Analyze the process of gel electrophoresis ■ Explain the process of gene cloning	**Lab Zone Think About It!** *Analyz-ing Gel Electrophoresis Results*, p. 211	**Unit 2 Review Module** ■ Section Review 9.2 ■ Interpreting Graphics 9 **Laboratory Manual,** Lab 18: "Extraction of DNA" **Consumer Applications** 9-1 **Biotechnology Manual** ■ Concepts of Biotechnology: Concepts 2, 3, and 5 ■ Lab 8: "Separating Dyes by Electro-phoresis ■ Lab 9: "Vegetable Electrophoresis" ■ Lab 11: "Analyzing DNA Fingerprints" ■ Lab 14: "Modeling Gene Transfer with a Plasmid" ■ Lab 15: "Bacterial Transformation with pBLU®Plasmid"
9.3 Applications of Genetic Engineering **Objectives** ■ Describe applications of genetic engineering ■ Compare the techniques used in these applications	**Lab Zone Do It!** *How Big Is the Human Genome?* p. 215 **In the Community** *Biotech Bulletin*, p. 216 **Everyday Biology** *Little Clues of You*, p. 217 **Lab Zone Investigate It!** *Modeling DNA Probes*, p. 218	**Unit 2 Review Module** ■ Section Review 9.3 ■ Activity Recordsheets 9-1 and 9-2 ■ Critical Thinking Exercise 9 ■ Enrichment Topic 9-1 **Biotechnology Manual,** Concepts of Biotechnology 4
9.4 Safety and Ethics in Biotechnology **Objectives** ■ Appraise the safety issues and precautions taken in biotechnology ■ Contrast the benefits and concerns associated with genetic engineering	**Lab Zone Do It!** *How Can Ethical Questions Be Answered?* p. 220 **STS: Issues in Biology** *Ethical Questions*, p. 220	**Unit 2 Review Module** ■ Section Review 9.4 ■ Activity Recordsheet 9-3 ■ Vocabulary Review 9 ■ Chapter 9 Tests **Issues and Decision Making** 9-1 and 9-2 **Biotechnology Manual,** Issues and Decisions 2 and 3

Technology Resources

Internet Connections

Within this chapter, you will see the  logo. If you and your students have access to the Internet, the following URL address will provide various Internet connections that are related to topics and features presented in this chapter:

http://genetics.biosurf.com

You can also find relevant chapter material at **The Biology Place** address:

http://www.biology.com

CD-ROMs

Biología: la telaraña de la vida,
  (Spanish Student Edition) Chapter 9
Teacher's Resource Planner, Chapter 9
  Supplements
Interactive Biological Simulations
■ Genetic Engineering
TestWorks CD-ROM
■ Chapter 9 Tests

Videodiscs

Animated Biological Concepts Videodiscs
■ Gene Transfer and Cloning
■ Transformation

Overhead Transparencies

■ Gene Cloning, #21

Videotapes

Biology Alive! Video Series
Rewind: The Web of Life Reteach Videos

Planning for Activities

STUDENT EDITION
Lab Zone
Discover It! p. 205
  ■ ink pad
  ■ plain paper
  ■ tracing paper
  ■ thin black marker

Lab Zone
Do It! p. 215
  ■ calculators

Lab Zone
Investigate It! p. 218
  ■ graph paper
  ■ pencil
  ■ scissors
  ■ a partner

TEACHER'S EDITION
Quick Activity, p. 206
Traits of breeds
  ■ poster showing dog breeds

Quick Activity, p. 209
Genetically engineered vegetables
  ■ broccoflower
  ■ paper
  ■ pencil

Teacher Demo, p. 212
Model of a bacterium in genetic engineering
  ■ metric ruler
  ■ two-three meters one-color yarn
  ■ small circles of yarn of other colors

Teacher Demo, p. 213
A transgenic tomato
  ■ transgenic tomato

Quick Activity, p. 219
Favorable traits
  ■ paper
  ■ pencil

Breeding
Section Review

The Big Idea!

Genotypes can be changed through selective breeding and genetic engineering. 9.1–9.2

Concepts

- Humans have practiced selective breeding of plants and animals for centuries.
- Outbreeding is the crossing of two different breeds and can result in hybrid vigor.
- Biotechnology is the use of living organisms to make products.

Words

selective breeding   inbreeding   outbreeding

PART A   *Match each term in Column B with its description in Column A. Write the letter of the correct term on the line provided.*

COLUMN A

_____   **1.** breeding organisms to produce certain desirable traits in offspring

_____   **2.** using living organisms to make new products useful to humans

_____   **3.** type of breeding in which organisms of similar genotype are crossed to maintain a desirable set of traits

_____   **4.** organism that is homozygous for desirable traits

_____   **5.** effect exhibited by an organism that is larger or healthier due to the breeding of distantly related parents

_____   **6.** type of breeding in which genetically distant organisms are crossed

COLUMN B

a. hybrid vigor

b. inbreeding

c. outbreeding

d. selective breeding

e. purebred

f. biotechnology

PART B

1. Explain the process of selective breeding.

_____

_____

_____

2. What is an example of selective breeding practiced by ancient peoples in North and South America?

_____

_____

3. How do inbreeding and outbreeding differ?

_____

_____

_____

4. What are the disadvantages of inbreeding?

_____

_____

_____

5. Give two examples of animals produced by outbreeding.

_____

_____

6. What are the advantages and disadvantages of outbreeding?

_____

_____

_____

7. Why have wildlife managers introduced Texas cougars into populations of the endangered Florida panther?

_____

_____

_____

8. Why are seed banks important?

_____

_____

Genetic Engineering
Section Review

9.2

∙∙

The Big Idea!

Genotypes can be changed through selective breeding and genetic engineering. 9.1–9.2

Concepts

- Genetic engineering refers to any technique used to identify or change DNA sequences.
- Scientists use gel electrophoresis to determine the sequence of DNA bases and to obtain DNA fingerprints.
- Recombinant DNA is a combination of the genetic material of two different breeds.
- Genes can be cloned using recombinant technology.

Words

genetic engineering   restriction enzymes   DNA fingerprint   recombinant DNA   vector
plasmids

PART A   *Complete the following definitions by writing the correct term from the Data Bank on the line provided.*

Data Bank		
genetic engineering	insulin	vector
plasmids	recombinant DNA	gel electrophoresis
restriction enzymes	DNA fingerprint	

1. The human hormone _____ is an example of a protein synthesized from recombinant DNA.

2. A(n) _____ is a carrier of genetic material.

3. The use of special biological techniques to identify or change genes at the molecular level is called _____ .

4. _____ is DNA with components of different organisms.

5. Small circular pieces of DNA within bacteria are known as _____ .

6. Genetic researchers often use _____ to sort DNA fragments by size.

7. Proteins that break DNA bonds at precise locations, known as _____ , are important tools in genetic engineering.

8. Every DNA sample has a unique pattern, called a(n) _____ , that can be used for identification.

PART B

1. What are sticky ends?

_____

_____

_____

2. Give an example of an application of gel electrophoresis.

_____

_____

_____

3. Why are yeast and bacteria important to genetic engineering?

_____

_____

_____

PART C *Place the steps of the cloning of the human insulin gene in sequential order. Write the correct letter on the line provided.*

1. _____   **a.** The recombined plasmid is inserted into a bacterial cell.

2. _____   **b.** Human DNA fragments are combined with plasmid DNA.

3. _____   **c.** Human and plasmid DNA are cut with restriction enzymes.

4. _____   **d.** Complementary sticky ends of human and plasmid DNA are produced.

5. _____   **e.** The recombinant bacterium reproduces, making clones of the human insulin gene.

Interpreting Graphics

Genetic Engineering and Recombinant DNA

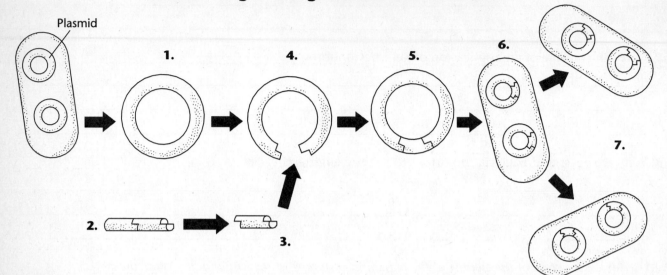

Plasmid

1.

2.

3.

4.

5.

6.

7.

PART A *Explain what is shown in each of the numbered steps in the diagram. Write your descriptions on the lines provided.*

1. _____
_____
_____
_____

2. _____
_____
_____
_____

3. _____
_____
_____
_____

4. _____
_____
_____
_____

5. _____
_____
_____
_____

6. _____
_____
_____
_____

7. _____
_____
_____
_____

PART B *Answer the following questions.*

1. What is a plasmid?
_____

2. What is recombinant DNA?
_____

3. Why do you think the genetic engineering process shown in the diagram is sometimes called gene splicing?
_____
_____
_____

Unit 2 Review Module   **87**

Applications of Genetic Engineering

Section Review

9.3

....

The Big Idea!

Technology enables us to find out about genotype and use this knowledge to affect phenotype. 9.3–9.4

Concepts

- Genetic engineering has current and potential applications in agriculture, industry, medicine, and forensics.
- Genetic engineering enables scientists to perform gene therapy, develop medicines, diagnose disorders, and study genomes.

Words

transgenic organisms

PART A

1. What are transgenic organisms?

_____

_____

2. Give an example of a way that genetic engineers are working to improve livestock.

_____

_____

_____

3. List two ways that genetic engineers have used recombinant DNA to modify crop plants.

_____

_____

_____

4. How has genetic engineering been used to improve cheese?

_____

_____

_____

_____

NAME _____ CLASS _____ DATE _____

PART B *Match each disease in Column B with its genetically engineered treatment or potential treatment described in Column A.*

COLUMN A

_____ **1.** protein that binds to specific types of cells to carry radioactive tracers or medicine to abnormal cells

_____ **2.** protein under development that causes blood to clot

_____ **3.** healthy genes combined with viruses or carrier cells to replace abnormal genes that cause excess mucus secretion

_____ **4.** genetically engineered bacteria to dissolve blood clots

_____ **5.** human gene is inserted into bacteria, which then mass produce a human hormone

COLUMN B

a. hemophilia

b. diabetes

c. cystic fibrosis

d. cancer

e. heart disease

PART C

1. What is the advantage of using insulin produced by genetically engineered bacteria to treat diabetes?

_____

_____

2. How is genetic engineering used to diagnose Huntington Disease?

_____

_____

3. Why is gene mapping important to genetic engineers?

_____

_____

4. How can genetic engineering techniques be used to solve crime?

_____

Do It! How Big Is the Human Genome?

Activity Recordsheet

9-1

■ ■

The Human Genome Project is possible only through the cooperative efforts of many scientists worldwide. You can find out just how much information researchers need to complete the project if you . . .

Try This

1. Choose a page from one of your textbooks that has only text, no illustrations.

2. Count the number of characters (all letters, numbers, punctuation, and spaces) in five lines of text. Divide this number by 5; your result is the average number of characters per line.

3. Count the number of lines on the page. Multiply the number of lines by the average number of characters per line. Your result is the average number of characters on a page.

4. Each character represents a DNA base. Divide the average number of characters per page by 2 in order to represent the number of "base pairs" per page.

5. Determine the number of pages in your textbook, and multiply that number by the number of base pairs per page. How many base pairs are in the textbook?

6. The human genome has about 3 million base pairs. How many books would you need to store all that information?

Analyze Your Data

1. If you stacked all the textbooks you would need to store the Human Genome Project, how tall would the stack be?

_____

2. Research the number of stars in the Milky Way. How does this number compare with the number of base pairs in the human genome?

_____

_____

_____

Investigate It! Modeling DNA Probes

Activity Recordsheet

9-2

▪▪

Propose a Hypothesis

Propose a hypothesis regarding the similarities or differences among the DNA sequences of individuals.

_____

_____

_____

_____

> **What You Will Do**
> *Use DNA sequences to identify individuals.*
>
> **Skills You Will Use**
> *Making models, classifying, organizing*
>
> **What You Will Need**
> *Graph paper, pencil, scissors, a partner*

Conduct Your Experiment

1. The DNA sequences for five individuals are shown in the figure.

Individual 1	ATCTCGAGACTGATTGGCCATAAGCTCGAG
Individual 2	ATTGGCCACTCGAGACGTTGGCCAAGTCCG
Individual 3	ATGACCATGGCCAGGCTCGAGCTGATGACG
Individual 4	ATATGGCCATTGCTCGAGTGGCCAGATCCG
Individual 5	ACTCGAGGTCCCTCGAGTGATGGCCATACG

Copy the DNA sequences onto graph paper, putting one letter from the DNA sequence into each square.

2. Look for DNA sequences in each individual that are complementary to this six-base DNA probe: TCCGAG.

3. Circle any DNA sequence in each individual that is complementary to the sequence of the DNA probe.

4. Record the numbers of the individuals who were identified by the DNA probe.

5. Choose one of the five individuals, and construct a new DNA probe that will identify only that individual. Write out the DNA sequence of the probe, and exchange it with a new sequence written by your partner.

6. Repeat steps 2 and 3 to identify the unknown individual, using the DNA probe that your partner constructed.

Analyze Your Data

1. What DNA sequence is the complement of the DNA probe shown in step 2?

_____

2. Which individual(s) was (were) identified by the DNA probe given in step 2?

_____

3. What is the complementary DNA sequence of the DNA probe from your partner (step 5)?

_____

4. Which individual(s) was (were) identified by the DNA probe from your partner?

_____

NAME _____ CLASS _____ DATE _____

Draw Conclusions

Explain how a person can be identified by a DNA probe. Is it possible for more than one individual to be identified by a DNA probe? Would a DNA probe with longer or shorter sequences be more likely to identify only one individual? Write a paragraph discussing the answers to these questions.

_____

_____

_____

_____

_____

_____

Design a Related Experiment

On the lines below, design an experiment to model how restriction enzymes could be used to create DNA fingerprints for the five individuals shown. Before writing your experiment, consider the fact that restriction enzymes cut DNA sequences at specific base pairs.

_____

_____

_____

_____

_____

_____

_____

Gene Therapy
Critical Thinking 9

THE SKILL: Analyzing Processes

When you analyze a complex process, you break it down into all of its parts. You identify the role each part plays in the overall process. You recognize relationships that exist among all the parts of the process. By examining each part of the process, you develop a greater understanding of the system as a whole. Read more about analyzing processes by turning to page 950 of your textbook.

Gene therapy is a process by which scientists use recombinant DNA to act in place of unhealthy DNA. In 1990, the U.S. National Institutes of Health approved gene therapy experiments aimed at correcting certain types of genetic diseases. The first human gene therapy experiment involved a 4-year-old girl suffering from a rare disease called ADA deficiency. Due to a defective gene, the cells in her immune system were unable to produce the chemical adenosine deaminase, or ADA. Without this necessary substance, toxins built up in her immune cells, damaging them so that they could not reproduce.

In an effort to correct the faulty gene that caused the disease, scientists inserted a healthy ADA gene into an altered retrovirus. The retrovirus had been genetically altered so that it would not cause illness. They extracted some of the girl's immune system cells and mixed them with the retrovirus. The retrovirus invaded these cells, carrying the healthy ADA gene into the DNA of the damaged cells. The immune system cells multiplied, complete with the healthy ADA gene. Once a month over a two-year period, healthy immune system cells were injected into the patient, and her body began producing ADA! After the initial two years of gene therapy, with continued therapy every six months, the girl is living a healthy, active life.

APPLICATION   *Write a complete answer to each question.*

1. On a separate piece of paper, make a flow chart to illustrate the steps in the gene therapy process described in the passage.

2. Why is the patient healthy and active after gene therapy?

   _____

   _____

   _____

3. Explain why gene therapy is said to be "a new and experimental method of fighting disease."

   _____

   _____

4. Viruses are major causes of disease. Yet, in this process, a virus was deliberately mixed with cells from the girl's immune system. Why do you suppose she didn't become ill?

   _____

   _____

   _____

Treating Diabetes
Enrichment Topic

9-1

▪ ▪

Diabetes was described as early as 1500 B.C. in an ancient document called the Egyptian Egers Papyrus. Early Greek physicians gave diabetes its name because of its symptoms. Diabetes means siphon or fountain. A person with untreated diabetes needs to urinate constantly.

Other symptoms of diabetes include thirst, hunger, weight loss, and blurred vision. Diabetes is a chronic disease, caused by either a lack of the hormone insulin or by the body's inability to use the insulin it produces. Insulin is normally manufactured in a small cluster of cells in the pancreas called the Islets of Langerhans.

Before insulin was discovered, the only treatment for diabetes was a very strict diet that was low in calories and carbohydrates. This type of diet lengthened the lives of diabetic patients, but, without insulin, the patients still died within a few

years. In 1921, two Canadian researchers discovered insulin. Today, patients taking insulin can live a normal life span. However, insulin does not cure diabetes, it only provides a chemical that the body is missing.

Until 1982, diabetics used insulin derived from the pancreases of pigs or other farm animals. At times this treatment posed problems because some patients were allergic to pig insulin or other animal insulin.

In 1966, insulin was synthesized by both an American biochemist and by biochemists in the People's Republic of China. The United States Food and Drug Administration (USFDA) approved synthetic human insulin in 1982. The insulin is artificially produced using recombinant DNA techniques. Synthetic human insulin is produced in bacteria, using gene-splicing methods.

EVALUATION   *Review the information you have been given about synthetic insulin. Then choose one of the topics below to research. Write an essay on your findings. If you need additional space, continue on a separate piece of paper.*

- Although synthetic insulin was first made in 1966, it was not approved by the USFDA until 1982. Research what happened during the years between the first synthesis of insulin and final approval. Were people in other countries using synthetic insulin?
- There are two types of diabetes, Type 1 and Type 2. Both are kinds of *diabetes mellitus*, rather than *diabetes insipidus*. Research the causes of Type 1 and Type 2 diabetes and the treatments for each.
- Research the use of synthetic insulin (trade name: Humilin) in diabetics. Who uses synthetic insulin rather than animal-derived insulin? Why? Which type of insulin is more expensive? You may want to search the World Wide Web, or interview a doctor or someone at a drug company (many have 800 numbers). You could also contact the Juvenile Diabetes Foundation, 60 Madison Ave, New York, NY 10010, or at http://www.jdfcure.com/.

_____

_____

_____

_____

_____

_____

_____

_____

_____

_____

Safety and Ethics in Biotechnology
Section Review

9.4

. . . .

The Big Idea!

Technology enables us to find out about genotype and use this knowledge to affect phenotype. 9.3–9.4

Concepts

- Scientists are addressing concerns about the safety of creating and releasing genetically engineered organisms.
- Potential applications of genetic engineering, such as the alteration of human genes, raise ethical questions for members of society to consider.

PART A

1. What are some potential problems that people fear could arise as a result of genetic engineering?

_____

_____

_____

_____

2. What steps have scientists taken to prevent a genetically engineered organism from being released into the environment?

_____

_____

_____

_____

3. What might be the long-term effects of releasing genetically engineered organisms into the environment?

_____

_____

_____

_____

4. Identify an abuse that could result from altering human genes.

_____

_____

_____

_____

PART B   *Read the following scenarios. Identify possible problems that could result from the genetic technology described, and then describe how these problems could be prevented.*

1. Some people experience severe allergic reactions to certain chemicals found in Brazil nuts, and thus must avoid any food that contains Brazil-nut products. Because all packaged food must contain a list of ingredients, avoiding foods that contain Brazil nuts is relatively easy. Brazil nuts are very high in protein. Scientists have spliced a gene from Brazil nuts into soybean plants to boost their protein content. Soybeans are a major feed crop for livestock.

   _____

   _____

   _____

   _____

   _____

2. Genetic engineers have developed crop plants highly resistant to herbicides. This enables farmers to use herbicides to kill weed plants without harming the desirable crop species. Crop plants may hybridize with closely related plants, passing the herbicide-resistant gene to native species.

   _____

   _____

   _____

   _____

3. An insurance company requires genetic screening of new applicants. The company has the right to deny insurance to applicants with a genetic predisposition to develop cancer and heart disease.

   _____

   _____

   _____

Do It! How Can Ethical Questions Be Answered?

Activity Recordsheet

9-3

∙∙

The ethical questions raised by biotechnology have no "right" or "wrong" answers but are decided by society as a whole. You can model the information-gathering process of government officials if you . . .

Try This

1. Choose three safety or ethical issues related to genetic engineering. Design a survey to ask people their opinions on the issues. Your questions may have a format similar to the sample question.

> I support keeping personal
>
> genome information private.
>
> (check one)
>
> ☐ Strongly agree
> ☐ Agree somewhat
> ☐ Disagree somewhat
> ☐ Strongly disagree

2. Find 15 people who will complete your survey. Collect the surveys and tabulate the answers.

Analyze Your Data

1. Was there total agreement on any issue? If more people were surveyed, would there be more or less agreement in the responses?

_____

_____

_____

2. How informed about biotechnology issues were the people you surveyed? If you were a politician or government official, how would you act upon the results of this survey?

_____

_____

_____

_____

Vocabulary Review

9

Select the term from the following list that best answers each question.

- restriction enzyme
- genetic engineering
- transgenic organism
- outbreeding
- DNA fingerprint
- recombinant DNA
- inbreeding
- selective breeding

1. What helped create certain breeds of dogs and cats? Farmers have also used this for years.

_____

2. What is the crossing of organisms that have a similar genotype? Sometimes, however, it creates major health problems.

_____

3. What often results in hybrid vigor? Some examples of it are a mule and a liger.

_____

4. What breaks DNA bonds at precise locations?

_____

5. From *Jurassic Park* to gel electrophoresis, what up-and-coming process changes genes at the molecular level?

_____

6. One day we may all be recognized by our birth name and this unique characteristic. Gel electrophoresis helps you see this characteristic.

_____

7. What is created when you transfer the gene for making human insulin into a bacteria? Vectors help make the transfer.

_____

8. What is created by the addition of a gene from a different species? Hopefully, they are bigger and tastier.

_____

The Biotechnology Revolution
Chapter 9

■ ■

Test A

Choose the best answer for each question and write its letter on the line provided.

_____ **1.** What genetic disorder causes the secretion of excess mucus?
    a. sickle-cell disease   **c.** Huntington disease
    b. cystic fibrosis   **d.** Tay-Sachs disease

_____ **2.** Selective breeding is the breeding of animals or plants to produce
    a. biotechnology   **b.** inbreeding   **c.** desired traits   **d.** outbreeding

_____ **3.** People with Huntington disease develop deterioration of the
    a. brain and nervous system   **c.** reproductive organs
    b. circulatory system   **d.** heart

_____ **4.** In genetic engineering, the carrier of genetic material is known as the
    a. recombinant DNA   **c.** enzyme
    b. plasmid   **d.** vector

_____ **5.** A liger (a cross between a male lion and a female tiger) is an example of
    a. outbreeding   **b.** inbreeding   **c.** cloning   **d.** polyploidy

_____ **6.** Small, circular pieces of DNA within bacteria are called what?
    a. vectors   **b.** plasmids   **c.** genetic engineers **d.** clones

_____ **7.** What disorder causes excessive bleeding due to the inability of blood to clot?
    a. Tay-Sachs   **b.** cystic fibrosis   **c.** hemophilia   **d.** sickle-cell anemia

_____ **8.** The use of special biochemical techniques to modify genes is called
    a. cross breeding   **c.** technical engineering
    b. genetic engineering   **d.** outbreeding

_____ **9.** The test for Huntington disease is a search for a section of DNA called a
    a. code   **b.** base   **c.** gene map   **d.** marker

_____ **10.** Which term describes the crossing of organisms that have a similar genotype?
    a. outbreeding   **b.** cross fertilization **c.** inbreeding   **d.** gene mixing

_____ **11.** Which term describes a genetic engineering technique that allows the sequencing of DNA bases?
    a. gel electrophoresis   **c.** transcription
    b. gene splicing   **d.** DNA marker

_____ **12.** Recombinant DNA is a combination of DNA from
    a. different genes of the same organism **c.** different organisms
    b. bacteria   **d.** viral material

_____ **13.** What are the most common organisms used for genetic engineering?
    a. sheep   **b.** bacteria   **c.** monkeys   **d.** viruses

_____ **14.** Scientists use DNA fingerprinting to solve crimes and
    a. establish family relationships   **c.** create new genetic diseases
    b. recreate ancient organisms   **d.** date the age of geological formations

_____ **15.** Hybrids that have parents from different species are usually
    a. blind   **b.** variant   **c.** sterile   **d.** unhealthy

_____ **16.** How can gene therapy help cystic fibrosis patients?
    a. by replacing faulty genes with healthy genes
    b. by introducing mucus-resistant bacteria into the lungs
    c. by engineering faulty proteins
    d. by creating virus-resistant genes

_____ **17.** How do genetic engineers ensure the safety of their work?
    a. by engineering organisms that cannot survive outside the laboratory
    b. by wearing protective gear to guard against infection
    c. by properly disposing of laboratory wastes
    d. all of the above

_____ **18.** Genetically engineered proteins that bind only to certain types of cells may be useful in the treatment of
    a. birth defects   **b.** hemophilia   **c.** cancer   **d.** Huntington disease

_____ **19.** What is one of the dangers of inbreeding?
    a. offspring with recessive alleles for undesirable traits and dominant alleles for desirable traits
    b. offspring that are healthier than the parents but sterile
    c. offspring that are homozygous for undesirable traits
    d. offspring without the desired traits

_____ **20.** Scientists can help people with heart disease by genetically engineering bacteria that
    a. slow down the heart rate   **c.** make insulin
    b. make a protein that clears clogged arteries   **d.** raise HDL cholesterol levels

_____ **21.** Unlike the insulin extracted from farm animals, genetically engineered insulin causes no
    a. allergic reactions   **c.** change in human blood chemistry
    b. metabolism of sugar   **d.** sleeplessness

_____ **22.** The fact that a mule, a cross between a male donkey and a female horse, is hardier than a horse is an example of
    a. crossing over   **b.** specialization   **c.** hybrid vigor   **d.** natural selection

_____ **23.** Which of the following is *not* a use for transgenic organisms?
    a. processing sewage   **c.** cleaning up toxic-waste dumps
    b. sterilizing cattle   **d.** making fuel oil from plants

_____ **24.** What do genetic engineers use to cut DNA at a specific series of base pairs?
    a. restriction enzymes   **c.** proteins
    b. insulin   **d.** DNA polymerase

_____ **25.** What term describes a genetically engineered tomato that ripens slowly?
    a. outbreed tomato   **c.** transgenic tomato
    b. tomato plasmid   **d.** regenerated tomato

The Biotechnology Revolution

Chapter 9

■ ■

Test B

Read each question or statement and respond on the lines provided.

1. The following descriptions are examples of controlled breeding. Identify each example as selective breeding, inbreeding, or outbreeding. *(15 points)*

   a. An orange is crossed with a grapefruit. _____

   b. Cows that mature quickly are permitted to reproduce while the others are not. _____

   c. Two closely related cats are bred to produce offspring with desirable traits. _____

2. Explain what is meant by the following terms used in genetic engineering. *(20 points)*

   a. recombinant DNA

   _____

   b. vector

   _____

   c. plasmid

   _____

   d. restriction enzyme

   _____

3. Suppose you are a scientist trying to help people who cannot produce an enzyme needed for proper digestion. How could you use biotechnology to produce bacteria to make the enzyme? *(20 points)*

   _____

   _____

   _____

   _____

   _____

   _____

4. Describe one example of an application of genetic engineering in each of the following areas. *(15 points)*

   a. agriculture _____

   b. industry _____

   c. medicine _____

5. a. Suppose a restriction enzyme recognizes the six-base sequence AAGCTT. Draw a line on the DNA sequences below to show where the enzyme will cut each fragment. *(5 points)*

A   A   G   C   T   T
T   T   C   G   A   A

b. Which of the two DNA fragments below would travel farther in electrophoresis gel? *(5 points)*

_____

Fragment A   **Fragment B**

6. Genetic engineering has raised many important ethical issues. Suppose that a new kind of virus is being developed to attack and kill specific kinds of bacteria. *(20 points)*

a. What benefits might result from such a development?_____
_____

b. What potentially serious problems might this development cause? _____
_____

c. Describe steps that might be taken to control these problems._____
_____
_____

d. Explain why dangers might still remain despite safety precautions. _____
_____
_____

Unit 2
Lab Practical Exam
6
∙ ∙

Goal

At this station, you will construct Punnett squares to predict the genotypes and phenotypes of offspring.

Materials

sheets of paper with Punnett squares and questions

Procedure

In the *Drosophila* fruit fly, *W* represents the allele for long wings, and *w* represents the allele for short wings. Long wings are dominant, short wings are recessive. Use Punnett squares to predict the outcome of four different crosses of fruit flies. Write an appropriate genotype of your choice for each parent above each square. In the second cross of long-winged and long-winged parents, write a different combination of genotypes than the first cross. Next to each square, write a ratio expressing the predicted relationship of long wings to short wings in the phenotypes of the offspring.

Long-winged Parent: _____   Long-winged Parent: _____
Long-winged Parent: _____   Long-winged Parent: _____

Long-winged Parent: _____   Short-winged Parent: _____
Short-winged Parent: _____   Short-winged Parent: _____

Analyze Your Results

1. Which crosses produce offspring with identical genotypes? Explain.

_____

_____

2. Which crosses produce offspring with identical phenotypes? Explain.

_____

_____

3. Do the ratios you found represent actual or probable outcomes? Explain the difference between the two.

_____

_____

Unit 2
Lab Practical Exam
7

••

Goal

At this station, you will analyze chromosomes in order to develop a human karyotype and to identify potential chromosomal abnormalities.

Materials

scissors   metric ruler

Procedure

Use the materials listed to make a human karyotype of the human chromosomes shown in the drawings on the right. Then compare the karyotype to the one on the left.

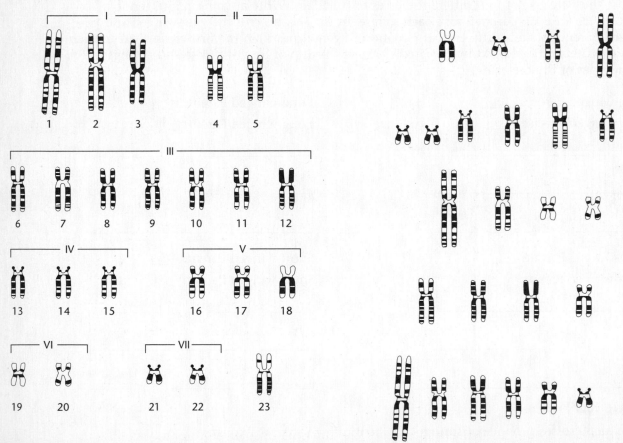

Analyze Your Results

1. Describe any abnormalities you may have found in the karyotype. For each abnormality you find, explain how the abnormality might have occurred, and what the effect of the abnormality would be on a human.

_____

_____

2. What else can you tell about the individual possessing the chromosomes in the karyotype? Explain.

_____

_____

Unit 2

Lab Practical Exam

8

Goal

At this station, you will analyze the effects of the environment and gene expression in tobacco seedlings.

Materials

two petri dishes containing tobacco seedlings

Safety

Wear safety goggles and be careful of breakage when working with the Petri dishes.

Procedure

Observe the tobacco seedlings in each of the Petri dishes. The seedlings in one dish were exposed to light, while the seedlings in the other dish were kept in darkness for the same amount of time. Note any differences in appearance among the seedlings in each dish. Record your observations in a data table that you create in the space below. Express your observations as percentages.

Analyze Your Results

1. Which dish do you think was exposed to light? How do the tobacco seedlings that have been exposed to the light differ from those kept in the dark?

_____

_____

_____

2. Is exposure to light the only factor that influences the color of the seedlings? Explain.

_____

_____

_____

3. How would you explain the influence of light and dark on the seedlings in terms of gene expression?

_____

_____

_____

4. Why is it important to report your observations as percentages?

_____

_____

_____

Unit 2 Genetics—Lab Practical Exams

Teacher's Notes
■ ■

Lab Practical Exam 6

PROCEDURE

Check to make sure students remember to write a ratio next to each Punnett square.

Lab Practical Exam 7

Review with students what a karyotype is.

PROCEDURE

Check to make sure students have matched each chromosome in the karyotype to at least one identical chromosome to the right.

Lab Practical Exam 8

Provide two Petri dishes for students to observe. Dish 1 contains carbon agar with 20 tobacco seedlings (albino and green mixed) that have been exposed to light for a period of 7 to 10 days. Dish 2 contains carbon agar with 20 tobacco seedlings (albino and green mixed) that have been exposed to darkness for a period of 7 to 10 days.

SAFETY

Remind students to wear safety goggles.

PROCEDURE

Give each pair of students the same amount of time, about 3 minutes, to study the contents of the Petri dishes.

Answer Key

■ ■

Section Review 6.1
PART A
1. The study of genetics is the scientific study of heredity.
2. A trait is a characteristic that can be passed from parent to offspring.
3. Mendel studied pea plants because of their structure, the presence of distinctive traits, and their rapid reproductive cycle.
4. A purebred receives the same genetic traits from both its parents. A hybrid receives different genetic traits from both its parents.
5. A dominant trait will appear or be expressed in an F_1 hybrid. A recessive trait will not.
6. Blending was the idea that parents contributed some sort of inheritable material to the production of the off-spring that was blended to produce the characteristics observed in the offspring.
7. In 25 percent of the F_2 generations the recessive traits were expressed.

PART B
1. m   **5.** e
2. b   **6.** l
3. c   **7.** I
4. j   **8.** f

Enrichment Topic 6-1
Answers may vary. A sample answer: Mendel's experiments with genetics were performed before or simultaneous with Weismann's work. Weismann's writings were recognized while Mendel's remained unnoticed at the time. However, today Mendel is considered the father of genetics. Mendel's extensive experiments were more thorough than Weismann's.

Enrichment Topic 6-2
Answers should show the double-cross hybridization technique. The four plants are crossed as A/B and C/D, and then A/B is crossed with C/D, to make ABCD.

Section Review 6.2
PART A
1. homozygous   **4.** homozygous
2. green pods   **5.** *Gg*
3. *gg*   **6.** green pods

PART B
1. An uppercase letter represents a dominant allele. A lowercase letter represents a recessive allele.
2. Genotype is all the alleles that produce a particular trait, while phenotype is the outward expression of that trait.
3. A plant with the genotype *GG* will have green pods, as will a plant with the genotype *Gg*.
4. The Law of Segregation states that gene pairs separate during meiosis, with each gamete receiving one gene from a homologous pair.
5. The Law of Dominance states that when an organism is heterozygous for a trait, the dominant allele is expressed and the recessive allele is hidden.
6. According to the Law of Independent Assortment, different traits are inherited independently.

PART C
1. Law of Dominance
2. Law of Segregation
3. Law of Independent Assortment

Section Review 6.3
PART A
1. Probability is the likelihood that an event will occur.
2. a. The probability of an event occurring is two out of three.
   b. The probability of an event occurring is four out of five.
3. Probability is useful in biology for predicting the phenotypes and genotypes in breeding experiments.

PART B
1. $\frac{1}{2}$. The F_1 plant will receive one *G* allele from the *GG* parent and the probability is $\frac{1}{2}$ that it will receive a *g* allele from the other parent.
2. $\frac{1}{4}$. The probability that the F_1 plant will receive a *g* allele is $\frac{1}{2}$ for each parent. The likelihood of receiving *g* alleles from both parents is $\frac{1}{2}$ x $\frac{1}{2}$, or $\frac{1}{4}$.
3. $\frac{1}{2}$. The probability of receiving a *G* allele from the first parent and a *g* allele from the second parent is $\frac{1}{4}$. The probability of receiving a *g* allele from the first parent and a *G* allele from the second parent is also $\frac{1}{4}$. Therefore, the probability that the F_1 plant will have the genotype *Gg* is $\frac{1}{4}$ + $\frac{1}{4}$, or $\frac{1}{2}$.

PART C
Figure I
1. *FF*   **3.** *Ff*
2. *Ff*   **4.** *ff*
Figure 2
1. *FFSS*   **9.** *FfSS*
2. *FFSs*   **10.** *FfSs*
3. *FfSS*   **11.** *ffSS*
4. *FfSs*   **12.** *ffSs*
5. *FFSs*   **13.** *FfSs*
6. *FFss*   **14.** *Ffss*
7. *FfSs*   **15.** *ffSs*
8. *Ffss*   **16.** *ffss*

PART D
1. A monohybrid cross examines only one trait at a time. A dihybrid cross examines the inheritance of two traits at the same time.
2. A test cross is the crossing of a known recessive genotype and an unknown genotype, resulting in offspring with observable phenotypes. Test crosses allow scientists to distinguish between homozygous dominant and heterozygous organisms.
3. 3   **7.** *FFSS, FfSS, FfSs, FFSs*
4. 1   **8.** 3
5. 3 : 1   **9.** 1
6. 1 : 2 : 1   **10.** 9 : 3 : 3 : 1

Interpreting Graphics 6
1. Check students' Punnett square for accuracy. This monohybrid cross will produce a genotypic ratio of 1 : 1.
2. Check students' Punnett square for accuracy.

Answer Key
■ ■

3. *Yy*

4. A monohybrid cross studies only one trait. A dihybrid cross studies two traits.

5. Green seed color is dominant.

6. Round seeds are dominant.

7. *YY, Yy*

8. yellow

9. 2

10. 2

11. 4

12. 8

13. tall, round; tall, wrinkled; short, round; short, wrinkled

14. A phenotype is the way a trait appears. A genotype includes both the dominant and recessive alleles.

Section Review 6.4
PART A
1. e   **4.** d

2. a   **5.** b

3. c

PART B
1. recessive genetic disorder

2. Huntington disease

3. Geneticists interview family members and friends of the family to collect as much information as they can about a family's genetic history and traits.

4. The information found in the pedigree can show the probability of one or both parents carrying a defective allele. This allows geneticists to determine the probability of the offspring inheriting the condition.

PART C
1. Regina, Jose, Gwen, Alex

2. Michael, Carlos, Selena, John, Pedro, Anibal

3. Alkaptonuria is a recessive disorder. Those with one copy of the allele are carriers and do not express the trait.

Critical Thinking 6
1. No. The only genotype that will cause albinism is *aa*.

2. Five members of the second generation have normal coloring while one shows albinism.

3. It is unlikely that their offspring will exhibit albinism. Because the male parent is homozygous dominant for the trait, it is impossible for any offspring to inherit a recessive gene from each parent.

4. Individuals III-3 and III-4 show the disorder. This occurs because both offspring inherited a recessive gene for the trait from each parent.

5. The spouse would have to have genotype *AA* to ensure that no offspring have albinism. If the spouse had genotype *Aa* or *aa*, it would be possible for a child to inherit a recessive gene from each parent.

Enrichment Topic 6-3
Answers will vary according to the breed chosen. A sample answer: There are different hypotheses about the origin of the Newfoundland breed. Some people believe that Newfoundlands were bred from Nordic dogs brought to Newfoundland in the 1600s. Others believe that the breed originated in Britain in 1700, when Newfoundland became

part of Britain. This theory says Newfoundlands were bred in Newfoundland from Tibetan mastiffs and local dogs. Other people think the Newfoundland is related to the Labrador. The dogs look similar. Labrador dogs could have come across the frozen Strait of Belle Isle to Newfoundland. Newfoundlands are large, strong, agile dogs. Their heavy hair is particularly suited to the cold Newfoundland weather. This breed is an excellent water rescue dog and was possibly bred for that purpose.

Section Review 6.5
PART A
1. In intermediate inheritance, a heterozygous individual has a phenotype that is not exactly like either purebred parent.

2. In incomplete dominance, a heterozygote displays a phenotype that is intermediate between two homozygous phenotypes. In codominance, both alleles in the heterozygote express themselves fully.

3. Accept all logical responses. Likely responses may include pink snapdragons.

4. Accept all logical responses. Likely responses may include human blood type AB.

5. A polygenic trait is a trait controlled by two or more gene pairs.

PART B
1. c   **4.** e

2. a   **5.** b

3. d

PART C
1. Low body temperatures cause the rabbit's fur to darker in color. Because the rabbit's extremities are usually colder than the rest of its body, the extremities are dark while the body is white.

2. Likely answers include flower color in hydrangeas and wing color in the western white butterfly.

3. "Nature or nurture" refers to the question of whether inheritance of a trait is affected more by genetics or by environment.

Enrichment Topic 6-4
1. Albinism is a genetic disorder. Several defects can cause albinism: lack of melanocytes, interference in embryonic cell migration, lack of tyrosinase, or cell abnormalities. The gene is recessive.

2. Essays may vary. Different cultures may have very different attitudes about albinism. Some cultures hold albino animals sacred and simultaneously consider albino people outcasts. Further, some cultures with darker skin thought the first Europeans they saw were albinos, and they were therefore either suspicious or positively impressed.

Vocabluary Review 6
1. recessive

2. traits

3. hybrid

4. chromosome theory of heredity

5. genotype

6. phenotype

Answer Key

■■ **■■ 109**

7. homozygous
8. Punnett square
9. pedigree
10. genes

Chapter 6 Test A

1. b	**14.** a
2. c	**15.** d
3. d	**16.** c
4. a	**17.** a
5. c	**18.** b
6. d	**19.** d
7. a	**20.** a
8. c	**21.** c
9. b	**22.** b
10. c	**23.** a
11. b	**24.** b
12. a	**25.** c
13. d	

Chapter 6 Test B

1. a. The original plants were purebred because self-fertilization yielded the same phenotypes.
   b. All the plants in the F_1 generation were hybrid.
   c. The gene for white flower color is recessive, and the gene for blue flower color is dominant.
   d. We would expect $\frac{3}{4}$ (75 percent) of the plants to be blue, and $\frac{1}{4}$ (25 percent), of the plants to be white.
2. a. The Law of Dominance states that the dominant allele will be expressed if it is present. Although all the offspring carry the white allele, the brown phenotype is expressed.
   b. The Law of Independent Assortment states that gene pairs separate independently of one another. Thus, all possible combinations of pairs of genes will occur.
   c. The Law of Segregation states that pairs of homologous chromosomes separate during meiosis. Thus, an organism that is heterozygous for a given trait will produce gametes with each allele.
3. a. homozygous, white
   b. homozygous, gray
   c. heterozygous, gray
   d. There are two phenotypes: white fur and gray fur.
4. a. This is a dihybrid cross because two traits are being studied at one time, height and flower color.
   b. 1. *TTRR* 2. *TTRr* 3. *TtRR* 4. *TtRr* 5. *TTRr* 6. *Ttrr* 7. *TtRr* 8. *Ttrr* 9. *TtRR* 10. *TtRr* 11. *ttRR* 12. *ttRr* 13. *TtRr* 14. *Ttrr* 15. *ttRr* 16. *ttrr*
   c. The phenotypic ratios will be 9 : 3 :3 : 1 for the phenotypes: tall/red, tall/white, short/red, and short/white.
5. A polygenic trait is a trait affected by more than one pair of genes. Pleiotropy is one gene affecting more than one trait.
6. a. codominance
   b. multiple alleles
   c. incomplete dominance

Section Review 7.1

PART A
1. The mouse died.
2. The mouse lived.
3. The mouse lived.
4. The mouse died.

PART B
1. *Streptococcus pneumoniae*, the bacterium that causes pneumonia
2. Strain S has a smooth mucous coat and causes pneumonia in mice. Strain R has a rough appearance with no mucous coat and does not cause pneumonia in mice.
3. (1) Griffith injected mice with live S bacteria and the mice got pneumonia. (2) Griffith injected mice with live R bacteria and the mice were unaffected. (3) Griffith killed S bacteria with heat then injected the dead bacteria into mice. The mice were unaffected. (4) Griffith injected mice with live R bacteria mixed with heat-killed S bacteria. The mice got pneumonia.
4. Griffith concluded that material had somehow been passed from the heat-killed strain S bacteria to the live strain R bacteria, transforming the R bacteria into S bacteria.
5. Scientists were not sure if the transferred material, the molecule of heredity, was DNA or protein.
6. Avery found that the only thing necessary for the transformation of strain R bacteria was DNA from strain S bacteria.

PART C
1. Bacteria did not become radioactive.
2. Bacteria became radioactive.

PART B
1. a. bacteriophage virus
   b. Phage viruses are made only of protein and DNA.
2. Chase and Hershey discovered that the bacteria infected with phages with radioactive protein were not radioactive. The bacteria infected with phages containing radioactive DNA were radioactive.
3. Chase and Hershey concluded that DNA, not protein, must be the hereditary material.

Section Review 7.2

1. g	**7.** c
2. g	**8.** a
3. t	**9.** a
4. c	**10.** c
5. a	**11.** t
6. t	**12.** g

PART B
1. In cells, the amount of adenine is always equal to the amount of thymine, and the amount of guanine is always equal to the amount of cytosine.
2. Franklin photographed DNA using X-rays.
3. A nucleotide consists of a five-carbon sugar, a phosphate group, and a nitrogenous base.
4. Adenine and guanine are purines, while cytosine and thymine are pyrimidines. Purine molecules are larger than pyrimidine molecules.

Answer Key

■ ■

5. The X-ray photographs made by Franklin and Wilkins revealed that the DNA molecule was wide and tightly coiled, with a spiral shape. Watson and Crick saw that the molecule was too thick to be a single strand. They experimented with several models before developing the double-helix model.

6. a. Enzymes break apart the weak bonds that hold the nitrogenous base pairs together, splitting apart the two strands of the DNA molecule.

b. Free nucleotides in the nucleus bond with their complementary bases on each exposed strand.

c. Bonds form between the sugars and phosphates of the free nucleotides to build a new backbone. Two complete strands of DNA are formed.

PART C

1. b   **4.** a
2. f   **5.** c
3. e   **6.** d

Interpreting Graphics 7
PART A

1. The allele for hemophilia is recessive. The female child with hemophilia must have received this allele from both parents. The genotype for the female child with hemophilia is X^hX^h. The genotype for the female child without hemophilia is X^hX. Since this child possesses only one recessive allele, she is a carrier of the disease.

2. The allele for hemophilia is carried only on the X chromosome. Since a male child only has one X chromosome, a male child will develop the disease if the recessive allele is present.

PART B

1. This chromosome indicates the presence of the recessive hemophilia allele.

2. Students should draw a square around b, d, and f. They should draw a circle around a, c, and e.

3. Students should shade in half of a and c.

4. Students should shade in f.

5. f

6. none

7. a, c

8. Hemophilia is a sex-linked trait because the allele that causes this disorder is carried on the sex chromosomes.

Critical Thinking 7

1. The author assumed that most readers think that DNA is the only chemical substance involved in the passing of traits from parent to offspring.

2. One might assume that since DNA and RNA have similar functions in the body, their chemical composition is the same.

3. The table shows variations in the components of DNA and RNA, disproving an assumption that they are chemically identical.

4. One might assume that every time a cell divides, its RNA is copied and passed to daughter cells.

Enrichment Topic 7-1

Answers may vary. Example: It is disgraceful that Franklin was never recognized and, in fact, never knew of her contribution to Watson and Crick's DNA models. While the study of science involves the work of more than one person, all contributions that lead to end results should be recognized. Wilkins may have believed that Franklin's work was his work, if he believed she was working for him. However, he took her photographs secretly, never told her of her contribution, and took credit for the project himself. Wilkins may have made additional contributions that made him worthy of the collective Nobel Prize. Ethics, however, should have inspired him to recognize Franklin's contributions, even posthumously.

Section Review 7.3
PART A

1. In these experiments, sweet pea plants that were homozygous dominant for flower color and pollen shape were crossed with plants that were homozygous recessive for these two traits. Bateson and Punnett then allowed the F_1 generation to self-fertilize.

2. The F_2 generation did not show the expected $9 : 3 : 3 : 1$ phenotype ratio. The two parental phenotypes showed up much more often than was expected.

3. Bateson and Punnett concluded that the genes for flower color and pollen shape did not sort independently. They suspected that the genes were connected and tended to stay together when gametes were formed.

4. Morgan discovered that the traits for body color and wing shape did not sort independently.

5. No. Mendel's Law of Independent Assortment only applies to genes on different chromosomes.

6. Linked genes are genes located on the same chromosome.

7. Linked genes do not sort independently, and as a result of being linked together, tend to be inherited together.

8. No. Pieces of homologous chromosomes sometimes cross over during meiosis, resulting in new chromosome combinations.

PART B

1. Check students' diagrams. *A* and *a* on the middle two chromatids should have crossed over.

2. The genes for hair color and eye color are closer on the chromosomes.

3. Hair color and eye color are most likely to be inherited together.

4. The genes for hair texture and eye color are more likely to be separated by crossing over because they are farther apart on the chromosome.

5. Crossing over is important because it results in new genetic combinations in offspring.

6. Recombinant offspring are those with new combinations of genes.

7. Geneticists compare the number of recombinant offspring to the number of offspring in which no crossing over occurred. These numbers make it possible to calculate how often recombination occurs between two gene pares. Since recombinations occur more frequently between genes that are far apart on the chromosome, a gene map can be constructed.

Answer Key

- ▪ ▪ ▪ ▪

Section Review 7.4
PART A
1. X and Y chromosomes

2. Sex chromosomes determine the sex of the individual and the sex-linked traits. The autosomes control all other traits. X and Y chromosomes are not homologous.

3. During meiosis, the sex chromosomes, like the autosomes, segregate. As a result, half the male's sperm cells carry an X chromosome and half carry a Y chromosome. Since females have two X chromosomes, all the eggs carry an X chromosome. The sex of the offspring is thus determined by the male gamete.

4. Fruit flies are easy to maintain, they reproduce quickly, they produce numerous offspring, and they only have four pairs of chromosomes.

5. Morgan crossed a red-eyed female with the white-eyed male. The F_1 generation offspring all had red eyes. Morgan crossed males and females from the F_1 generation to produce an F_2 generation.

6. All the white eyed flies were male.

7. A sex-linked trait is a trait that is controlled by a gene on a sex chromosome.

PART B
1. a. $X^C Y$
   b. $X^c Y$
   c. $X^c X^c$
   d. $X^C X^C$
   e. $X^C X^c$

2. $X^C X^c$ x $X^c Y$

$X^C X^c$	$X^C Y$
$X^c X^c$	$X^c Y$

3. a. None of the male children are colorblind.
   b. None of the female children are colorblind.

4.

$X^C Y$	$X^c Y$
$X^C X^c$	$X^c Y^c$

5. a. 50 percent
   b. None of the female children are colorblind.

6. The allele for colorblindness is carried on the X chromosome and is recessive. Since a father only contributes Y chromosomes to his sons, he cannot pass on colorblindness to his sons.

7. Colorblindness is more common in males than in females because the Y chromosome has no allele to counteract the X-linked colorblind allele.

PART C
1. Sex-linked traits are controlled by genes on the sex chromosomes. Sex-limited traits are controlled by genes on autosomes and activated by the hormones of one sex, but not the other.

2. Sample answers include colorful plumage on male birds, beard growth in human males, and milk production in human females.

3. Sex-influenced traits are expressed in both sexes, but are expressed differently.

4. A sample response is baldness.

Section Review 7.5
PART A
1. c	**4.** a
2. d	**5.** e
3. b	**6.** f

PART B
1. To make a karyotype, scientists use chemicals to freeze cells at the metaphase stage of cell division, when chromosomes are easy to isolate, stain, and photograph.

2. The karyotype is used to find any chromosomal abnormalities that are visible, such as too many or two few chromosomes, as well as to study chromosome shape, structure, and size.

3. Likely answers include Down syndrome.

PART C
1. Accept all logical responses. Likely responses may include: healthier plants, stronger plants, larger flowers, larger fruits.

2. In animals, polyploidy almost always results in death.

3. Likely responses include wheat, potatoes, and oats.

4. Down Syndrome, caused by trisomy of chromosome 21.

5. This is a project in which researchers hope to map all the genes in human DNA. Geneticists hope to map the positions of about 90,000 genes.

6. The Human Genome Project will provide information about human genes and how they might be manipulated, including genes responsible for disease.

7. Detractors question the usefulness of a human gene map, citing the fact that much of an organism's DNA has no apparent function.

Vocabulary Review 7
1. b	**5.** a
2. c	**6.** b
3. d	**7.** c
4. b	**8.** a

Chapter 7 Test A
1. a	**14.** a
2. b	**15.** c
3. c	**16.** d
4. b	**17.** d
5. a	**18.** b
6. c	**19.** a
7. a	**20.** c
8. c	**21.** d
9. d	**22.** a
10. b	**23.** b
11. d	**24.** d
12. b	**25.** b
13. c	

Answer Key

■ ■

Chapter 7 Test B

1. a. Griffith determined that the exchange of genetic material transforms organisms. He found that when heat-killed virulent bacteria were mixed with live nonvirulent bacteria, the virulence was transferred to the live bacteria.

b. Chase and Hershey proved that the genetic material of organisms was composed of DNA and not protein. Their method was to radioactively label both the DNA and protein of bacteriophages, and mix the phages with bacteria. They observed that only the DNA was injected into the bacteria.

2. a. A nucleotide is composed of a phosphate group, a nitrogenous base, and a five-carbon sugar.

b. The four bases are adenine, thymine, cytosine, and guanine. Adenine and thymine are a complementary pair as are cytosine and guanine.

c. The sugars and phosphates form the backbone of the DNA molecule.

d. Bonds between pairs of complementary nitrogenous bases join the two DNA strands together to form the double helix. During DNA replication, the weak bonds between complementary bases are broken and the two strands "unzip." Unattached bases then move in and bind to their complementary bases on the newly freed strands.

3. Monosomy results from the fusion of a normal gamete with a gamete that lacks a copy of a chromosome due to nondisjunction. Trisomy results from the fusion of a normal gamete with a gamete that has two copies of a chromosome due to nondisjunction. The best way to detect suspected monosomy or trisomy is with a karyotype. This study produces a photograph of the chromosomes in which the absence or duplication of chromosome can be seen.

4. a. This trait is sex-influenced because it is expressed in both sexes, but differently.

b. This trait is sex-limited because it only occurs in one gender.

c. This trait is sex-linked (specifically it is X-linked) because the gene for the trait is on a sex chromosome.

5. a. You would expect all offspring to have fringed petals and orange stamens.

b. The expected phenotype ratio would be 9 : 3 : 3 : 1, because the chromosomes sort independently in accordance with Mendel's law.

c. If both genes are on the same chromosome, then F and O always occur together and f and o always occur together because the original plants were homozygous. A Punnett square shows that with no crossing over the F_2 generation will be $\frac{3}{4}$ fringed with orange stamens and $\frac{1}{4}$ non-fringed with yellow stamens.

6. The purpose of the Human Genome Project is to determine the base sequence of all the genes on all the chromosomes in the human body. The importance of the project lies in the fact that a map of the human genome will be a valuable tool for further study and possible manipulation of human chromosomes.

Section Review 8.1
PART A

1. h	**6.** e
2. a	**7.** b
3. d	**8.** f
4. c	**9.** g
5. i	

PART B

1. g	**6.** a
2. b	**7.** e
3. d	**8.** i
4. h	**9.** c
5. j	

PART C

1. Accept all logical responses. Likely responses may include the fact that their structure is different, RNA contains uracil instead of thymine, and DNA and RNA contain different sugar groups.

2. A region of two DNA strands unwinds and separates. RNA polymerase matches unattached RNA bases to their complementary DNA bases, forming a string of RNA bases which join together to form molecule of RNA.

3. RNA splicing involves the rearrangement of the mRNA before it leaves the nucleus for translation. Segments of bases, called introns, that do not code for proteins are cut out by special enzymes. The remaining segments of code, called exons, are joined to produce the final mRNA.

4. In prokaryotes, mRNA travels directly to the ribosome. In eukaryotes, mRNA must first be spliced before it travels to the ribosome. Prokaryotes can therefore multiply very rapidly.

5. AUG, methionine

6. UAA, UAG, UGA

7. Elongation is the process by which a protein is assembled from individual amino acids. tRNA transports successive amino acids to their appropriate mRNA codons, forming a chain of amino acids.

Enrichment Topic 8-1

1. Amniocentesis is a screening technique used for high-risk pregnancies. Since it is an invasive procedure, there are some risks involved. If the fetus is not at high risk, amniocentesis is usually not used.

2. Chorion villus biopsy can be carried out 8 to 12 weeks after conception, so the mother can have results from the biopsy much earlier in her pregnancy than those resulting from amniocentesis. Cells form the chorionic membrane are obtained through the mother's abdomen or cervix. The main advantage to chorionic villus biopsy is the earlier results; the main disadvantage is that risk to the fetus may be slightly higher than that associated with amniocentesis.

Section Review 8.2
PART A

1. activated
2. deactivated
3. prokaryotes
4. eukaryotes, cell specialization

Answer Key

■ ■

5. selective gene expression
6. RNA splicing

PART B

1. The Jacob-Monod hypothesis describes how gene expression is controlled in bacteria by proteins that "turn off" genes.

2. A repressor protein bonds to DNA to block protein synthesis.

3. A promoter is a section of DNA that is the binding site of RNA polymerase, the enzyme that causes the two DNA strands to separate.

4. The repressor protein binds to the DNA, blocking the binding site of RNA polymerase. Because RNA polymerase cannot bind to the DNA, the two strands cannot separate and transcription is prevented.

5. When *E. coli* is in a lactose-rich environment, lactose binds to the repressor protein, changing its shape. The repressor protein can no longer bind to DNA, enabling RNA polymerase to bind with the promoter. *E. coli* begins to produce enzymes to digest lactose.

6. When lactose runs out, the repressor protein is once again free to bind with DNA, transcription stops, and *E. coli* stops producing the lactose enzymes.

7. In some bacteria, high levels of protein activate the repressors, causing them to bind with DNA and halt the production of more protein.

Section Review 8.3

PART A

1. e   **5.** c
2. b   **6.** d
3. f   **7.** a
4. g

PART B

1. The two main categories of mutations are chromosome mutations, which involve entire chromosomes, and gene mutations, which involve individual genes.

2. An example of a deletion mutation is the notched wing of the fruit fly.

3. Inversion mutations change the order but not the number of genes in a chromosome. Deletions and duplications change the number of genes in a chromosome, which is much more harmful to the organism.

PART C

1. no check mark   **5.** no check mark
2. ✔   **6.** no check mark
3. no check mark   **7.** ✔
4. ✔

PART D

1. Some amino acids are coded for by several codons. A point mutation may merely change one codon into another that codes for the same amino acid.

2. A point mutation could cause protein synthesis to halt by changing a codon in the middle of a gene into the "stop" codon.

3. Barbara McClintock noticed that color inheritance in corn did not follow normal patterns of inheritance. She discovered "jumping genes," or genes that change location on the chromosome.

Interpreting Graphics 8

PART A

1. A karyotype of a person with Down syndrome shows an extra chromosome at chromosome 21.

2. trisomy 21

3. There is an extra X chromosome. In males the genotype is *XXY* and in females the genotype is *XXX*.

4. trisomy X

5. Turner syndrome is a condition where there is only one X chromosome in females and no X chromosomes in males.

6. nondisjunction of X chromosomes

7. A section of a chromosome breaks off and reattaches upside-down.

8. inversion, deletion, nondisjunction

Section Review 8.4

PART A

1. True

2. An oncogene is a gene that causes a cell to become cancerous.

3. Retinoblastoma is caused by deletions to chromosome 13.

4. True

5. People who inherit the recessive mutation for retinoblastoma are predisposed to develop the cancer.

PART B

1. mutagen   **4.** base analogs
2. carcinogen   **5.** Ames Test
3. chlorofluorocarbons; UV radiation

PART C

1. In gene therapy, mutated genes are replaced with normal genes.

2. Accept all logical responses. Likely responses may include tars and other chemicals in cigarette smoke, UV radiation, certain chemicals in smoked meats, and viruses.

3. Accept all logical responses, including using sunscreen, regular mammograms, avoiding smoking, healthy eating habits, and a diet high in beta carotene.

Critical Thinking 8

1. Ultraviolet light is very intense. It penetrates the cell and alters or breaks sections of the DNA strands. This changes the genetic information carried on the DNA and the cells do not reproduce as they should.

2. The chemicals that help repair the damaged DNA are Uvr A, B, and C. ATP provides the energy needed for the repair.

3. Uvr A and Uvr B proteins unwind the DNA coil a section at a time. The damaged section is removed by the Uvr D protein, then DNA polymerases create a new section of DNA and insert it into the strand.

4. The factors that contribute to the development of basal cell carcinoma are old age and overexposure to the ultraviolet rays of the sun.

Vocabulary Review 8

1. Duplication. All others are integral parts of protein synthesis.

2. Mutagen. All others are involved in protein synthesis.

Answer Key

■ ■

3. Refrigerants. All others have been found in varying amounts to cause cancer.

4. Prokaryotic. All others are associated with RNA splicing.

5. Proteins. All others help ensure that amino acids are linked in the proper order.

6. Nucleus. All others are involved with chromosomal mutations.

7. Duplication. All others cause gene mutations.

8. Introns. All others are involved with cancer.

9. Mutation. All others are involved directly with protein synthesis.

10. Inversion. All others are involved directly with translating mRNA.

Chapter 8 Test A

1. a	**14.** c
2. c	**15.** b
3. d	**16.** d
4. b	**17.** c
5. a	**18.** b
6. b	**19.** d
7. c	**20.** c
8. b	**21.** d
9. a	**22.** c
10. d	**23.** b
11. a	**24.** c
12. c	**25.** a
13. a	

Chapter 8 Test B

1. a. This process, called transcription, results in the genetic information from DNA being copied into a strand of mRNA.

b. In eukaryotes, the transcribed mRNA must be spliced together. This step does not occur in prokaryotes.

c. This process is called translation. The base sequences in the mRNA code for specific amino acids, which are linked to build proteins.

2. a. frameshift mutation

b. mutagen

c. carcinogen

d. oncogene

e. deletion

f. gene mutation

g. point mutation

3. Although every cell contains the same chromosomes, not all genes are activated in every cell. Because different genes are active in different cells, different proteins are produced in different cells. Each cell uses its proteins to build cell organelles and structural components that allow the cell to complete its unique tasks in the organism. This leads to cell specialization and differentiation.

4. a. duplication

b. inversion

c. normal crossover

d. translocation

e. deletion

5. a. exon

b. intron

c. promoter

d. repressor

6. The three ways are: a mutation occurs in a gene for growth-factor proteins, multiple copies of a growth-factor gene may be made through errors in cell division, and a gene translocation results in more frequent transcription. Each of these situations can lead to uncontrolled cell division and growth.

Section Review 9.1

PART A

1. d	**4.** e
2. f	**5.** a
3. b	**6.** c

PART B

1. In selective breeding, organisms with certain desirable traits are selected to reproduce. The process is continued for successive generations until the desirable traits are well established in the population.

2. Ancient peoples in North and South America used selective breeding to develop corn and potatoes from wild plants.

3. Inbreeding is the crossing of organisms that have a similar genotype. Outbreeding is the crossing of distantly related organisms.

4. Inbred organisms have a greater chance of being homozygous for alleles that produce harmful traits or defects.

5. Likely responses may include mules and ligers.

6. In many cases, outbreeding can result in larger, healthier offspring. However, the offspring may be sterile because the nonhomologous chromosomes cannot undergo meiosis properly, and the hybrid cannot produce normal gametes.

7. Florida panther populations are so small that inbreeding is common, resulting in health problems. The Texas cougar was introduced to bolster the genetic variation of the panther.

8. Seed banks are important as resources for desirable plants, and for preventing the extinction of uncommon varieties of plants.

Section Review 9.2

PART A

1. insulin

2. vector

3. genetic engineering

4. recombinant DNA

5. plasmids

6. gel electrophoresis

7. restriction enzymes

8. DNA fingerprint

PART B

1. Sticky ends are created when restriction enzymes cut DNA at precise locations. Because the ends are open to new bonds, they are "sticky."

2. Correct responses include: the use of DNA fingerprints for identification purposes, to determine if a person carries a gene associated with a disorder, or to find the base-pair sequence of DNA strands.

3. Yeast and bacteria can be used to create clones of human genes by inserting human DNA fragments into yeast or bacteria DNA.

Answer Key

■ **Answer Key ■ 115 ■**

PART C
1. c
2. d
3. b

4. a
5. e

Interpreting Graphics 9

PART A
1. A plasmid is removed from a bacterial cell.
2. DNA is removed from a human cell.
3. The DNA is snipped for insertion into the plasmid.
4. The plasmid is snipped to make a place to insert the human DNA.
5. A recombinant DNA plasmid is formed.
6. The plasmid is inserted into a bacterial cell.
7. Bacteria reproduce and contain the human DNA inserted into the plasmid.

PART B
1. a small ring of DNA that carries genes of bacteria and is used in genetic engineering
2. a plasmid with a section of DNA from another organism spliced onto it
3. Part of the plasmid is removed and replaced by a splice of DNA from another organism.

Section Review 9.3

PART A
1. Transgenic organisms are organisms that have been altered by adding a gene from another species.
2. Accept all logical responses. Likely responses may include bacteria that produce a milk-stimulating hormone, and genes that increase meat production.
3. Answers will vary but may include changing the gene that stimulates ripening in tomatoes to prevent spoilage, and pest-resistant crops.
4. Chymosine, a substance that causes milk to coagulate, is produced by genetically engineered bacteria. Chymosine creates a smoother cheese.

PART B
1. d
2. a
3. c

4. e
5. b

PART C
1. Animal insulin causes allergic reactions in some diabetics. Insulin produced by genetically engineered bacteria does not.
2. The test for Huntington disease involves a search for a marker, a section of DNA that signifies the presence of the Huntington gene.
3. Genetic engineers can use gene mapping to locate specific genes on the chromosomes.
4. Because no two people have identical DNA (with the exception of identical twins), detectives can determine who was present at a crime by analyzing hair or skin samples found at the scene.

Critical Thinking 9
1. Flow charts should show extraction of a healthy human ADA gene, insertion into a retrovirus, mixing the retrovirus with the patient's immune system cells, the retrovirus invad-ing the patient's cells, duplication of the patient's cells complete with the gene for ADA production, and reinjection of the cells into the patient.
2. The patient is healthy and active because her immune system cells are now capable of producing ADA due to the procedure described in the passage.
3. Gene therapy is revolutionary in that it attempts to correct the original cause of a particular disease, namely, a faulty gene.
4. The virus has been altered genetically so that it doesn't kill cells or cause disease.

Enrichment Topic 9-1
Answers will vary. An example of what the second topic essay might cover: Type 1 *diabetes mellitus* occurs when the beta cells in the Islets of Langerhans no longer produce insulin. In Type 2 diabetes, the beta cells produce varying amounts of insulin, but the body cannot use those amounts effectively. Type 1 is also referred to as juvenile diabetes or insulin-dependent diabetes, and usually begins before age 30. Type 1 diabetes must be treated with regular insulin injections. Type 2 diabetes occurs mostly in middle age or during pregnancy. There are drugs for Type 2 diabetes that help the body make more effective use of the insulin it can produce. Type 2 diabetes can also treated with a special diet before insulin is prescribed as a last resort.

Section Review 9.4

PART A
1. Accept all logical responses. Likely responses may include the accidental release of harmful organisms into the environment.
2. Scientists adhere to strict laboratory procedures that prevent contact with or the escape of potentially harmful organisms. In addition, organisms can be altered so that they cannot survive outside the laboratory.
3. Answers will vary but should state that genetically engineered organisms could alter natural systems.
4. Answers may vary. Parents would be able to control the traits of their offspring, a practice that raises serious ethical issues.

PART B
1. Students should suggest that because the genetically engineered soybeans are used as livestock feed, proteins from the Brazil-nut gene could be passed on to cattle. Therefore, meat produced by the cattle could cause severe reactions in people allergic to Brazil nuts. This can be avoided by placing a warning on the meat stating that it may contain proteins from Brazil nuts.
2. Students may suggest that farmers would be dependent on chemical herbicides, or that the herbicide-resistant gene could be passed on to native weed plants. The herbicide would then be useless. This could be avoided by preventing plants from crossing with native species.
3. People with a history of cancer or heart disease would not be able to obtain insurance. This presents an ethical dilemma. Students may suggest that genetic screening is a form of discrimination, and that insurance companies should not be allowed access to an applicant's genetic history.

Answer Key

■ ■

Vocabulary Review 9

1. selective breeding
2. inbreeding
3. outbreeding
4. restriction enzymes
5. genetic engineering
6. DNA fingerprint
7. recombinant DNA
8. transgenic organisms

Chapter 9 Test A

1. b   14. a
2. c   15. c
3. a   16. a
4. d   17. d
5. a   18. c
6. b   19. c.
7. c   20. b
8. b   21. a
9. d   22. c
10. c   23. b
11. a   24. a
12. c   25. c
13. b

Chapter 9 Test B

1. **a.** outbreeding
   b. selective breeding
   c. inbreeding
2. **a.** Recombinant DNA is DNA made from the genetic material of two different organisms.
   b. A vector is used to carry genetic material from one host to another.
   c. A plasmid is a circular piece of DNA within bacteria.
   d. A restriction enzyme is a protein used to break DNA bonds at specific locations.
3. To engineer the bacteria, you would use recombinant DNA technology. First, cut the human gene for the enzyme and the bacterial plasmid with the same restriction enzyme. The enzyme gene is now incorporated into the plasmid. Insert the plasmid into a bacterial cell. In the bacterial cell, the enzyme will be produced as the gene is transcribed and translated along with the bacterial DNA. As the cell reproduces and clones itself, the human gene will also be copied.
4. Responses to this question will vary. The following are some likely responses:
   a. In agriculture, genetic engineering has led to the development of disease- and pest-resistant crops.
   b. In industry, genetically engineered bacteria have been used to help clean up toxic wastes and oil spills and to process sewage.
   c. In medicine, genetic engineering techniques are used to develop a range of gene therapies. One therapy uses cell-specific proteins to label abnormal cells to be targeted by medication. Another medical application is the development of tests for genetic diseases.
5. **a.**

A	A	G	C	T	T
T	T	C	G	A	A

b. The shorter DNA fragment, B, will move the farthest and fastest.
6. Responses will vary. Accept all logical responses.
   a. The virus might be designed successfully and effectively eradicate the harmful bacteria. This might then improve the quality of life for many people.
   b. The virus might turn out to be deadly. If it escaped from the laboratory it could cause illness or death. The virus might contaminate the water or food supply of a community or ecosystem.
   c. Precautions should be taken to prevent the virus from escaping from the laboratory. Lab workers should avoid direct contact with the virus so that they do not become contaminated.
   d. Even with these precautions, the long-term effects of the virus on the environment, the food chain, and other organisms will not be known for some time.

Lab Practical Exam 6

PROCEDURE

There are three different long-wing/long-wing crosses:
$WW \times WW$: all offspring are WW; all are long-winged.
$WW \times Ww$: $\frac{3}{4}$ are WW, $\frac{1}{4}$ are Ww; all are long-winged.
$Ww \times Ww$: $\frac{1}{4}$ are WW, $\frac{1}{2}$ are Ww, and $\frac{1}{4}$ are ww; the ratio of long-winged to short-winged phenotypes is 3 : 1.
There are two different long-wing/short-wing crosses:
$WW \times ww$: all are Ww; all are long-winged.
$Ww \times ww$: $\frac{1}{2}$ are Ww, $\frac{1}{2}$ are ww; the ratio is 1 : 1.
There is one possible short-wing/short-wing cross:
$ww \times ww$: all are ww, all are short-winged.

ANALYZE YOUR RESULTS

1. The $WW \times WW$, $WW \times ww$, and $ww \times ww$ crosses produce offspring with identical genotypes. Each parent has a single type of allele to contribute. Such a cross can produce only a singe genotype in the offspring.
2. All crosses that produce identical genotypes will produce identical phenotypes. In addition, $WW \times Ww$ will produce all long-winged offspring.
3. The ratios are possible outcomes. Possible outcomes are calculated predictions of what is likely to occur. Actual outcomes are those that have actually taken place.

Lab Practical Exam 7

ANALYZE YOUR RESULTS

1. There is a trisomy of chromosome 21, which results in Down syndrome. Trisomy occurs when there is nondisjunction in meiosis II. The chromatids do not separate, leading to an incorrect number of chromosomes in the resulting gametes. People with Down syndrome may be mildly or severely developmentally challenged.
2. The individual is a woman; there are two X sex chromosomes present.

Answer Key

- *Answer Key* - - - -

Lab Practical Exam 8

1. Data recorded in tables will vary. Check data tables for logical organization.

2. Percentages will vary. All seedlings kept in darkness will be colorless.

ANALYZE YOUR RESULTS

1. Dish 1 was exposed to light. Responses will vary depending on how many seeds of each type germinated. Some seedlings exposed to light will be green. Those kept in darkness will be colorless.

2. Some seedlings failed to turn green after exposure to light, so there must be another factor affecting color, such as genetic mutation.

3. Responses will vary. Students may say light and dark are stimuli that control the production of proteins that regulate the genetic expression of albinism and germination.

4. Using percentages enables an accurate comparison to be made of the appearance of the plants in each dish.